Reading and Note Taking Guide
Level A

PEARSON

Prentice Hall

Boston, Massachusetts
Upper Saddle River, New Jersey

To the Teacher
This Reading and Note Taking Guide helps your students succeed in their study of science. Working through the exercises will help them understand and organize the concepts presented in the textbook. The completed worksheets then become easy-to-follow study guides for test preparation.

This Reading and Note Taking Guide also helps students improve their study and reading skills. The section "Your Keys to Success" on pages 5–10 of this Guide describes English/Language Arts skills developed in the textbook. Distribute copies of this section for students to use as a reference when completing the worksheets. Students will find it a handy tool for becoming successful readers in science and other subjects.

ISBN 0-13-203441-7

1 2 3 4 5 6 7 8 9 10   09 08 07 06

Contents
Life Science

Your Keys to Success

How to Read Science

 The target reading skills introduced on this page will help you read and understand information in this textbook. Each chapter introduces a reading skill. Developing these reading skills is key to becoming a successful reader in science and other subject areas.

Preview Text Structure By understanding how textbooks are organized, you can gain information from them more effectively. This textbook is organized with red headings and blue subheadings. Before you read, preview the headings. Ask yourself questions to guide you as you read. (Chapter 1)

Preview Visuals The visuals in your science textbook provide important information. Visuals are photographs, graphs, tables, diagrams, and illustrations. Before you read, take the time to preview the visuals in a section. Look closely at the titles, labels, and captions. Then ask yourself questions about the visuals. (Chapter 2)

Sequence Many parts of a science textbook are organized by sequence. Sequence is the order in which a series of events occurs. Some sections may discuss events in a process that has a beginning and an end. Other sections may describe a continuous process that does not have an end. (Chapters 10 and 14)

Compare and Contrast Science texts often make comparisons. When you compare and contrast, you examine the similarities and differences between things. You can compare and contrast by using a table or a Venn diagram. (Chapters 9 and 12)

Analyze Cause and Effect A cause makes something happen. An effect is what happens. When you recognize that one event causes another, you are relating cause and effect. (Chapter 16)

Identify Main Ideas As you read, you can understand a section or paragraph more clearly by finding the main idea. The main idea is the most important idea. The details in a section or paragraph support the main idea. Headings and subheadings can often help you identify the main ideas. (Chapters 3, 6, and 15)

Identify Supporting Evidence Science textbooks often describe the scientific evidence that supports a theory or hypothesis. Scientific evidence includes data and facts, information whose accuracy can be confirmed by experiments or observation. A hypothesis is a possible explanation for observations made by scientists or an answer to a scientific question. (Chapter 7)

Create Outlines You can create outlines to help you clarify the text. An outline shows the relationship between main ideas and supporting details. Use the text structure—headings, subheadings, key concepts, and key terms—to help you figure out information to include in your outline. (Chapters 4 and 8)

Take Notes Science chapters are packed with information. Taking good notes is one way to help you remember key ideas and see the big picture. When you take notes, include key ideas, a few details, and summaries. (Chapters 5, 11, and 13)

⏻ Target Reading Skills

Each chapter provides a target reading skill with clear instruction to help you read and understand the text. You will apply the skill as you read. Then you will record what you've learned in the section and chapter assessments.

Before You Read
Each chapter introduces a target reading skill and provides examples and practice exercises.

As You Read
As you read, you can use the target reading skill to help you increase your understanding.

After You Read
You can apply the target reading skill in the Section Assessments and in the Chapter Assessments.

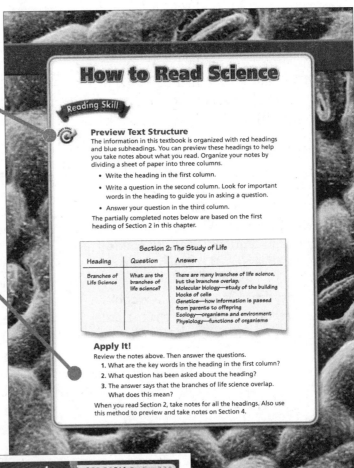

How to Read Science

Reading Skill

Preview Text Structure
The information in this textbook is organized with red headings and blue subheadings. You can preview these headings to help you take notes about what you read. Organize your notes by dividing a sheet of paper into three columns.

- Write the heading in the first column.
- Write a question in the second column. Look for important words in the heading to guide you in asking a question.
- Answer your question in the third column.

The partially completed notes below are based on the first heading of Section 2 in this chapter.

Section 2: The Study of Life

Heading	Question	Answer
Branches of Life Science	What are the branches of life science?	There are many branches of life science, but the branches overlap. Molecular biology—study of the building blocks of cells Genetics—how information is passed from parents to offspring Ecology—organisms and environment Physiology—functions of organisms

Apply It!
Review the notes above. Then answer the questions.
1. What are the key words in the heading in the first column?
2. What question has been asked about the heading?
3. The answer says that the branches of life science overlap. What does this mean?

When you read Section 2, take notes for all the headings. Also use this method to preview and take notes on Section 4.

Section 2 Assessment   S 7.5, 7.6 E-LA: Reading: 7.2.0

Target Reading Skill Preview Text Structure When you took notes on Section 2, what question did you ask for the heading Change Over Time? What was your answer?

Reviewing Key Concepts
1. a. **Defining** What is life science?
   b. **Describing** List three branches of life science and describe what is studied in each.
   c. **Making Judgments** Your friend wants to be a plant biologist and says she only needs to take courses in plant biology. Why might it be a good idea for your friend to study other branches of life science as well?
2. a. **Listing** What are four big ideas in life science?
   b. **Comparing and Contrasting** What are some ways that a cat and a tree are similar? What are some ways they are different?

Lab zone At-Home Activity

It's Complementary Explain to a family member what "complementary structure and function" means. Then look through books or magazines for photos of organisms that illustrate this concept. Find five examples to show your family member. Describe how a structure on each of the organisms is adapted to its function.

Build Science Vocabulary

 Studying science involves learning a new vocabulary. Here are some vocabulary skills to help you learn the meaning of words you do not recognize.

Word Analysis You can use your knowledge of word parts—prefixes, suffixes, and roots—to determine the meaning of unfamiliar words.

Prefixes A prefix is a word part that is added at the beginning of a root or base word to change its meaning. Knowing the meaning of prefixes will help you figure out new words. You will practice this skill in Chapters 3 and 9.

Suffixes A suffix is a letter or group of letters added to the end of a word to form a new word with a slightly different meaning. Adding a suffix to a word often changes its part of speech. You will practice this skill in Chapters 5 and 15.

Word Origins Many science words come to English from other languages, such as Greek and Latin. By learning the meaning of a few common Greek and Latin roots, you can determine the meaning of new science words. You will practice this skill in Chapters 2, 4, 12, and 13.

Use Clues to Determine Meaning
When you come across a word you don't recognize in science texts, you can use context clues to figure out what the word means. First look for clues in the word itself. Then look at the surrounding words, sentences, and paragraphs for clues. You will practice this skill in Chapters 8 and 11.

Identify Multiple Meanings
To understand science concepts, you must use terms precisely. Some familiar words may have different meanings in science. Watch for these multiple-meaning words as you read. You will practice this skill in Chapter 7.

Identify Related Word Forms
You can increase your vocabulary by learning related forms of words or word families. If you know the meaning of a verb form, you may be able to figure out the related noun and adjective forms. You will practice this skill in Chapter 16.

Vocabulary Skills

One of the important steps in reading this science textbook is to be sure that you understand the key terms. Your book shows several strategies to help you learn important vocabulary.

Before You Read

Each chapter introduces a Vocabulary Skill with examples and practice exercises. Key terms come alive through visuals. The beginning of each section lists the key terms.

Build Science Vocabulary

The images shown here represent some of the Key Terms in this chapter. You can use this vocabulary skill to help you understand the meaning of some Key Terms in this chapter.

Vocabulary Skill

Prefixes

Words can sometimes be divided into parts. A root is the part of the word that carries the basic meaning. A prefix is a word part that is placed in front of the root to change the word's meaning. In the word *multicellular*, for example, *-cellular* is the root and *multi-* is the prefix. The prefix *multi-* means "many." *Multicellular* means "having many cells."

The prefixes below will help you understand some Key Terms.

Prefix	Meaning	Example Word
chlor-	green	**chloroplast** A cellular structure that captures energy from sunlight
cyto-	cell	**cytoskeleton** The framework inside a cell
multi-	many	**multicellular** Having many cells
uni-	one	**unicellular** Having one cell

Apply It!
1. A **chloroplast** is a structure in plant cells. What color do you think a chloroplast is?
2. What clue within the word **cytoplasm** lets you know that the word has something to do with cells?

osmosis

Unicellular and Multicellular

Organisms may be composed of only one cell or many trillions of cells. **Unicellular**, or single-celled, organisms include bacteria (bak TIHR ee uh), the most numerous organisms on Earth. **Multicellular** organisms are composed of many cells.

🔵 In multicellular organisms, cells are often organized into tissues, organs, and organ systems. A **tissue** is a group of similar cells that work together to perform a specific function. For example, your brain is mostly made up of nervous tissue, which consists of nerve cells. An **organ**, such as your brain, is made up of different kinds of tissues that work together. In addition to nervous tissue, your brain contains other kinds of tissue that support and protect it. Your brain is part of your nervous system, an organ system that directs body activities and processes. An **organ system** is a group of organs that work together to perform a major function.

Unicellular

Multicellular

FIGURE 4
Cellular Organization
This dog is multicellular. The bacteria that live naturally on its teeth are unicellular. Each green sphere is a bacterial cell.

Reading Checkpoint What is an organ?

As You Read

Each key term is highlighted in yellow, appears in boldface type, and is followed by a definition.

Section 1 Assessment

S 7.1 E-LA: Reading 7.1.2, Writing 7.2.4

Vocabulary Skill Prefixes Complete the following sentences with Key Terms.
Because bacteria each have only one cell, they are _____ organisms.
Animals have many cells. Therefore, animals are _____ organisms.

🔵 **Reviewing Key Concepts**
1. a. **Defining** Define *structure* and *function*.
   b. **Explaining** Explain this statement: Cells are the basic units of structure and function in organisms.
   c. **Applying Concepts** In what important function are the cells in your eyes involved?
2. a. **Reviewing** What does a microscope enable people to do?
   b. **Summarizing** Summarize Hooke's observations of cork under a microscope.
   c. **Relating Cause and Effect** Why would Hooke's discovery have been impossible without a microscope?

3. a. **Listing** What does the cell theory state?
   b. **Explaining** What did Virchow contribute to the cell theory?
   c. **Applying Concepts** Use Virchow's ideas to explain why plastic plants are not alive.
4. a. **Reviewing** How do multicellular organisms differ from unicellular organisms?
   b. **Explaining** What is the relationship among cells, tissues, and organs?
   c. **Inferring** Would a tissue or an organ have more kinds of specialized cells? Explain.

Writing in Science

Writing an Award Speech Suppose you are a member of a scientific society that is giving an award to one of the early cell scientists. Choose the scientist, and write a speech that you might give at the award ceremony. Be sure to describe the scientist's accomplishments.

After You Read

You can practice the Vocabulary Skill in the Section Assessments. You can apply your understanding of the key terms in the Chapter Assessments.

Build Science Vocabulary

High-Use Academic Words

High-use academic words are words that are used frequently in classroom reading, writing, and discussions. They are different from key terms because they appear in many subject areas.

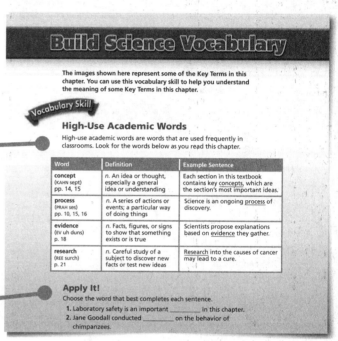

Learn the Words

Each unit contains a chapter that introduces high-use academic words. The introduction describes the words, provides examples, and includes practice exercises.

Practice Using the Words

You can practice using the high-use academic words in Apply It! and the Section Assessments.

Focus on Life Science High-Use Academic Words

Learning the meanings of these words will help you improve your reading comprehension in all subject areas.

adjust	contract	flexible	normal	section
adult	contrast	focus	obvious	sequence
affect	contribute	function	occur	series
alter	convert	identical	percent	source
analyze	cycle	indicate	predict	specific
approach	detect	interact	process	stable
area	determine	interpret	range	structure
attach	device	involve	region	survival
communicate	distinct	label	regulate	technique
complex	diverse	layer	require	theory
concept	enable	locate	research	transport
conduct	environment	maintain	resource	unique
consist	evidence	mature	respond	vary
constant	expose	method	reverse	visible

Investigations

You can explore the concepts in this textbook through inquiry. Like a real scientist, you can develop your own scientific questions and perform labs and activities to find answers. Follow the steps below when doing a lab.

1 Read the whole lab.

5 Record your data.

2 Write a purpose. What is the purpose of this activity?

3 Write a hypothesis. What is a possible explanation? Hypotheses lead to predictions that can be tested.

4 Follow each step in the procedure. Pay attention to safety icons.

Lab zone Skills Lab

Changing Colors

S 7.6.e, 7.7.c

Problem
How do color filters affect the appearance of objects in white light?

Skills Focus
observing, inferring, predicting

Materials
- shoe box
- scissors
- flashlight
- removable tape
- red object
  (such as a ripe tomato)
- yellow object
  (such as a ripe lemon)
- blue object
  (such as blue construction paper)
- red, green, and blue cellophane, enough to cover the top of the shoe box

Procedure
1. Carefully cut a large rectangular hole in the lid of the shoe box.
2. Carefully cut a small, round hole in the center of one of the ends of the shoe box.
3. Tape the red cellophane under the lid of the shoe box, covering the hole in the lid.
4. Place the objects in the box and put the lid on.
5. In a darkened room, shine the flashlight into the shoe box through the side hole. Note the apparent color of each object in the box.
6. Repeat Steps 3–5 using the other colors of cellophane.

Analyze and Conclude
1. Observing What did you see when you looked through the red cellophane? Explain why each object appeared as it did.
2. Observing What did you see when you looked through the blue cellophane? Explain.
3. Inferring What color(s) of light does each piece of cellophane allow through?
4. Predicting Predict what you would see under each piece of cellophane if you put a white object in the box. Test your prediction.
5. Predicting What do you think would happen if you viewed a red object through yellow cellophane? Draw a diagram to support your prediction. Then test your prediction.
6. Communicating Summarize your conclusions by drawing diagrams to show how each color filter affects white light. Write captions to explain your diagrams.

Design an Experiment
Do color filters work like pigments or like colors of light? Design an experiment to find out what happens if you shine a light through both a red and a green filter. *Obtain your teacher's permission before carrying out your investigation.*

6 Analyze your results. Answering the questions will help you draw conclusions.

7 Communicate your results in a written report or oral presentation. Your report should include
- a hypothesis
- a purpose
- the steps of the procedure
- a record of your results
- a conclusion

Lab Report

Purpose: To determine how color filters affect an object's appearance.

Hypothesis:

For more information on Science Inquiry, Scientific Investigations, and Safety refer to the Skills Handbook and Appendix A.

Thinking Like a Scientist

Key Concepts

■ What skills do scientists use to learn about the world?

Science is a way of learning about the natural world. **Scientists use skills such as observing, inferring, predicting, classifying, and making models to learn more about the world and make scientific progress. Observing** means using one or more of your senses to gather information. Your senses include sight, hearing touch, taste, and smell. Observations can be either quantitative or qualitative. **Quantitative observations** deal with a number, or amount. Seeing that you have eight new e-mails in your inbox is a quantitative observation. **Qualitative observations,** on the other hand, deal with descriptions that cannot be expressed in numbers. Noticing that a bike is blue and that a grape tastes sour are qualitative observations.

When you explain or interpret the things you observe, you are **inferring,** or making an inference. Making an inference doesn't mean guessing wildly. Inferences are based on reasoning from what you already know. **Predicting** means making a forecast of what will happen in the future based on past experience or evidence. While inferences are attempts to explain what is happening or *has* happened, predictions are forecasts, or what *will* happen in the future.

Classifying is the process of grouping together items that are alike in some way. Classifying helps you compare and contrast an organism's actions, behaviors, or functions. You classify objects and information all the time. Classifying things helps you to stay organized so you can easily find and use them later.

Making models involves creating representations of complex objects or processes. Models help people study and understand things that are complex or that can't be observed directly. Using a model allows scientists to share information that would otherwise be difficult to explain. Models include diagrams and physical objects, such as globes and movie sets. Some models are computer-generated, like the ones architects use to design new buildings. Models are only representations of a real object or process. Therefore, some information may be missing from a model.

A **scale model** accurately shows the proportions between its parts. A scale is a proportion used in determining the relationship of a model to the object that it represents. A scale model may be bigger or smaller than the object it represents.

What is Science? ▪ *Reading/Notetaking Guide*

Thinking Like a Scientist (pp. 6–12)

This section describes the skills scientists use to learn about the world.

Use Target Reading Skills

Before you read, preview the red headings in your text. For each heading, write a
what, how, *or* why *question in the left-hand column below. As you read, write
answers to your questions in the right-hand column.*

Scientific Skills

Question	Answer
What does observing involve?	Observing involves . . .

What is Science? · *Reading/Notetaking Guide*

Introduction (p. 6)

1. Is the following sentence true or false? Science is a way of learning about the natural world. _____

2. What are five skills scientists use to learn more about the world?

   a. _____ b. _____ c. _____

   d. _____ e. _____

Observing (p. 7)

3. What is observing?

   _____

   _____

4. The senses a scientist uses in observing include sight, hearing, touch, taste, and _____.

5. In the spaces below, define quantitative and qualitative observations. Give an example of each type of observation.

Observations	
Quantitative Observations	**Qualitative Observations**
Definition: **Example:**	**Definition:** **Example:**

Inferring (p. 8)

6. What is inferring?

   _____

   _____

What is Science? ▪ *Reading/Notetaking Guide*

Thinking Like a Scientist (continued)

7. Circle the letter of each item that is true about inferences.

   a. Inferences are based on reasoning from what you already know.

   b. Making an inference involves wild guessing.

   c. An inference is an interpretation of observations.

   d. People make inferences all the time.

Predicting (p. 9)

8. Making a forecast of what will happen in the future based on past experience or evidence is called _____.

9. How are inferring and predicting related?

   _____

   _____

   _____

Classifying (p. 10)

10. What is classifying?

    _____

    _____

    _____

11. Is the following sentence true or false? Classifying makes it easier to compare and contrast organisms and their actions, behaviors, or functions.

    _____

Making Models (pp. 11–12)

12. What does making models involve?

    _____

    _____

13. Circle the letter of each item that could be a model.

    a. map

    b. movie set

    c. computer-generated illustration

    d. notebook notes

What is Science? ▪ *Reading/Notetaking Guide*

14. Is the following sentence true or false? Models help people study things that cannot be observed directly. _____

15. Is the following sentence true or false? Some information about an object or process may be missing from a model. _____

16. What is a scale model?

_____

_____

17. What is a scale?

_____

_____

18. Circle the letter of each sentence that is true about scale models.

   a. A map may have a scale model with the proportion of one centimeter to one kilometer.
   b. A scale model is always smaller than the object it represents.
   c. A model may be built to different scales.

Chapter 1 What is Science? ▪ *Section 2 Summary*

The Study of Life

Key Concepts

- How are the branches of life science related?
- What are some big ideas in life science?

Life science is the study of living things. Another name for life science is biology. Biologists work in laboratories or outside, and they can work for universities, private companies, or government agencies. They usually work as part of a team.

Life science includes many branches, or fields of study. Molecular biology is the study of cells and of all life. Genetics is the study of how information about organisms is passed down from parent to offspring. Ecology is the study of how organisms interact with each other and their surroundings. Physiology is the study of the functions of organisms. **Though life science can be divided into branches, the different fields of study often overlap.** Progress in one field of life science often contributes to progress in another field.

Biologists recognize some big ideas in life science. (1) Organisms are diverse, yet share similar characteristics. (2) The structure and function of organisms are complementary. (3) Groups of organism change over time. (4) Organisms operate on the same physical principles as the rest of the natural world.

Living things come in a variety of shapes and sizes, but they have many basic similarities. All organisms are made up of tiny building blocks called cells. Cells carry out all the activities necessary for life. The chemical composition of all living things is remarkably similar. Every living thing is made up mainly of water. Most organisms contain DNA, which controls the activities of the cells and allows organisms to pass information to their offspring. All living things require energy. Living things can grow and develop. **Development** is the process of change that causes an organism to become more complex during its lifetime. Finally, all living things reproduce.

Because organisms respond to their surroundings, they must also adapt to changes in the environment in order to survive. The characteristics of any group of organisms can change over time. This gradual process is called evolution. Evolution helps to explain the diversity of organisms and the relationship between structure and function.

The form of all living things is closely related to the way that the organism lives. **Structure** is the way that an organism is put together as a whole. **Functions** are the processes that enable an organism to survive. Every organism's structure is adapted to help the organism carry out specific functions. Structure and function are **complementary,** which means that they work together to meet the needs of the organism.

Today scientists know that life follows the same rules, or principles, as the rest of nature. The principles of chemistry and physics help explain some life processes.

What is Science? ▪ *Reading/Notetaking Guide*

The Study of Life (pp. 13–17)

This section explains how the branches of life science are related and what some of the big ideas in life science are.

Use Target Reading Skills

Before you read, preview each red and blue heading, and ask a question to guide you as you read the topic. After you read, use the graphic organizer to take notes to help you answer your questions.

Heading	Question	Answer
Branches of Life Science	How are the branches of life science related?	

What is Science? · *Reading/Notetaking Guide*

The Study of Life *(continued)*

Introduction (p. 13)

1. What is life science?

    _____

Branches of Life Science (p. 14)

2. How do biologists work?

    _____

    _____

Match the branch of life science with its description.

Branches

_____ 3. molecular biology

_____ 4. genetics

_____ 5. ecology

_____ 6. physiology

Descriptions

a. the study of how information about organisms is passed down from parent to offspring

b. the study of the functions of organisms

c. the study of the tiny building blocks of cells and of all life

d. the study of how organisms interact with each other and with their surroundings

7. Is the following sentence true or false? Progress in one field of life science never affects or contributes to progress in another field. _____

Big Ideas in Life Science (pp. 15–17)

8. What are the four big ideas of life science?

    _____

    _____

    _____

    _____

9. What are five ways in which organisms are similar?

    _____

    _____

    _____

    _____

    _____

10. The process of change that causes an organism to become more complex during its lifetime is _____.

11. Circle the letter of each sentence that is true about evolution.
    a. Evolution is a process that occurs over many generations.
    b. Organisms don't need to adapt to their changing environments in order to survive.
    c. Evolution helps explain the diversity of organisms and the relationship between structure and function.
    d. Growth and development are the same as evolution.

12. How are structure and function related?

    _____

    _____

13. Is the following sentence true or false? Life follows the same principles as the rest of nature. _____

14. What functions in an organism can be explained by the principles of chemistry?

    _____

    _____

    _____

15. How do the principles of physics help explain the way animals see the world?

    _____

    _____

Scientific Inquiry

Key Concepts

- What is scientific inquiry?
- What makes a hypothesis testable?

Thinking and questioning can be the start of the **scientific inquiry** process. **Scientific inquiry refers to the diverse ways in which scientists investigate the natural world and propose explanations based on evidence they gather.** Scientific inquiry often begins with a problem or questions about an observation. Questions come from experiences you have and from observations and inferences you make. A scientific question is one that can be answered by making observations and gathering evidence.

A **hypothesis** is a possible explanation for a set of observations or answer to a scientific question. **In science, a hypothesis must be testable. This means that researchers must be able to carry out investigations and gather evidence that will either support or disprove the hypothesis.**

A scientist designs an experiment to test a hypothesis. All factors that can change in an experiment are called **variables.** The variable that is purposely changed to test a hypothesis is called the **manipulated variable** (also called the independent variable). The factor that may change in response to the manipulated variable is called the **responding variable** (also called the dependent variable). All other variables must be exactly the same. An experiment in which only one variable is manipulated at a time is called a **controlled experiment.** A **control** is part of the experiment to which you can compare the results of the other tests. In the control, the conditions are the same except for the manipulated variable. A well-designed experiment has clear operational definitions. An **operational definition** is a statement that describes how to measure a particular variable or define a particular term.

A controlled experiment produces data. **Data** are facts, figures, and other evidence gathered through observations. A data table is an organized way to collect and record observations. A graph can help you interpret data and reveal patterns or trends in data.

After gathering and interpreting data, a scientist draws conclusions about the hypothesis. A conclusion is a summary of what a scientist has learned from an experiment. In drawing your conclusion, you should ask yourself if you collected enough data and if your data supported your hypothesis.

An important part of the scientific inquiry process is communicating the results. **Communicating** is the sharing of ideas and experimental findings with others through writing and speaking.

Scientific inquiry usually doesn't end once a set of experiments is done and results are communicated. Often a scientific inquiry raises new questions, which lead to new hypotheses and experiments.

What is Science? · *Reading/Notetaking Guide*

Scientific Inquiry (pp. 18–22)

This section explains what a process called scientific inquiry is and what makes an explanation called a hypothesis testable.

Use Target Reading Skills

A definition states the meaning of a word or phrase by telling about its most important feature or function. After you read this section, reread the paragraphs that contain the definitions of the Key Terms. Use all the information you have learned to write a definition of each Key Term in your own words on the lines below.

scientific inquiry

_____

_____

hypothesis

_____

_____

variable

_____

_____

controlled experiment

_____

_____

manipulated variable

_____

_____

responding variable

_____

_____

control

_____

_____

operational definition

_____

_____

data

_____

_____

What is Science? ▪ *Reading/Notetaking Guide*

Scientific Inquiry *(continued)*

communicating

_____

_____

The Scientific Process (pp. 18–22)

1. What does scientific inquiry refer to?

    _____

    _____

    _____

    _____

2. Is the following sentence true or false? Scientific inquiry often begins
    with developing a hypothesis. _____

3. Circle the letter of each sentence that is a scientific question.
    a. At what temperature does water boil?
    b. When does the sun rise on April 3?
    c. How can my team work better together?
    d. Why does she like science more than he does?

4. A(n) _____ is a possible explanation for a set of
    observations or answer to a scientific question.

5. Is the following sentence true or false? Scientists consider a hypothesis
    to be a fact. _____

6. What is a testable hypothesis?

    _____

    _____

    _____

    _____

What is Science? · *Reading/Notetaking Guide*

7. To test a hypothesis, a scientist designs a(n) _____.

Match the term with its definition.

Term	Definition
____ 8. responding variable	**a.** a statement that describes how to measure a particular variable or define a particular term
____ 9. operational definition	**b.** the one variable that is purposely changed to test a hypothesis
____ 10. manipulated variable	**c.** a factor that can change in an experiment
____ 11. controlled experiment	**d.** the factor that may change in response to the manipulated variable
____ 12. variable	**e.** an experiment in which only one variable is manipulated at a time

13. Is the following sentence true or false? If you did not control variables in an experiment, there would be no way to know which variable explained your results. _____

14. In carrying out a controlled experiment, what does an operational definition do?

    _____

    _____

15. The facts, figures, and other evidence gathered through observations are called _____.

16. Circle the letter of each sentence that is true about graphs.

    a. A graph can reveal a trend in data.
    b. Graphs are the only way to organize data.
    c. A graph can reveal a pattern in data.

17. A(n) _____ is a summary of what you have learned from an experiment.

18. What might you ask yourself in drawing a conclusion about an experiment?

    _____

    _____

What is Science? · *Reading/Notetaking Guide*

Scientific Inquiry *(continued)*

Complete the Nature of Inquiry diagram by filling in the blanks.

The Nature of Inquiry

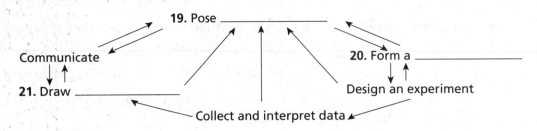

22. Why is scientific inquiry a process with many paths, not a rigid sequence of steps?

_____

_____

23. In scientific inquiry, what is communicating?

_____

_____

_____

24. Circle the letter of the sentence that explains why scientists describe their research in full when they communicate with other scientists.

   a. A scientific law requires scientists to pose questions.

   b. Other scientists need to be able to repeat a scientist's experiments.

   c. Scientists share their ideas in scientific journals.

Safety in the Laboratory

Key Concepts

- Why is preparation important when carrying out scientific investigations in the lab and in the field?

- What should you do if an accident occurs?

Good preparation helps you conduct careful scientific investigations by planning for safety. Preparing for a lab should begin the day before you will perform the lab. It is important to read through the procedure carefully and make sure you understand all the directions. Also, review the general safety guidelines in Appendix A of your textbook. When you perform the lab, always follow your teacher's instructions and the textbook directions exactly. Labs and activities in this textbook series include safety symbols. These symbols alert you to possible dangers in performing the lab and remind you to work carefully. The symbols are explained in Appendix A.

When you have completed the lab, be sure to clean up the work area. Turn off and unplug all equipment and return it to its proper place. Follow your teacher's instructions about proper disposal of wastes. Finally, be sure to wash your hands thoroughly after working in the laboratory.

Some investigations will be done in the "field." The field can be any outdoor area, such as a forest, park, or schoolyard. Just as in the laboratory, good preparation helps you stay safe when doing science activities in the field. There can be many safety hazards outdoors, including severe weather, traffic, wild animals, or poisonous plants. Planning may help you avoid some hazards. Whenever you do field work, always tell an adult where you will be. Never carry out a field investigation alone.

At any time, an accident may occur. **When any accident occurs, no matter how minor, notify your teacher immediately. Then, listen to your teacher's directions and carry them out quickly.** Make sure you know the location and proper use of all the emergency equipment in your lab room. Knowing safety and first aid procedures beforehand will prepare you to handle accidents properly.

What is Science? · *Reading/Notetaking Guide*

Safety in the Laboratory (pp. 23–26)

This section explains why preparation is important when carrying out scientific investigations. It also describes what you should do if an accident occurs.

Use Target Reading Skills

Before you read, preview each red and blue heading, and ask a question to guide you as you read the topic. After you read, use the graphic organizer to take notes to help you answer your questions.

Heading	Question	Answer
Safety During Investigations	Why is preparing before a lab important?	

Safety During Investigations (pp. 23–25)

1. Is the following sentence true or false? No amount of preparation can help you with safety when doing science activities in the laboratory. _____

2. Circle the letter of the time when preparing for a lab should begin.
   a. 1 hour ahead of the lab
   b. 10 minutes ahead of the lab
   c. the morning of the lab
   d. 1 day before doing the lab

3. In preparing for a lab, it is important to review the general safety guidelines, which can be found in _____ of your textbook.

What is Science? ▪ *Reading/Notetaking Guide*

4. What should you do if something is unclear to you about the lab before you begin?

   _____

   _____

5. Is the following sentence true or false? You should never try anything on your own in the lab without asking your teacher first. _____

6. Circle the letter of each sentence that is true about safety symbols.

   a. They identify safety equipment that you should use.
   b. They alert you to possible dangers in doing the lab.
   c. They give you specific instructions about each lab in the book.

Match the symbol with its meaning by writing the correct letter beside each symbol.

____ 7.

____ 8.

____ 9.

____ 10.

____ 11.

a. Sharp Object

b. Corrosive Chemical

c. Physical Safety

d. Breakage

e. Disposal

12. When you have completed a lab, you should _____ your work area.

13. How should lab wastes be disposed of?

    _____

    _____

    _____

    _____

14. Is the following sentence true or false? You should wash your hands after working in the laboratory even if you don't think they're dirty. _____

15. Circle the letter of each place that a science investigation might be done in the field.

    a. schoolyard
    b. classroom
    c. forest
    d. park

16. Is the following sentence true or false? Good preparation helps you stay safe when doing science investigations in the field. _____

What is Science? • *Reading/Notetaking Guide*

Safety in the Laboratory *(continued)*

17. Complete the concept map below to show some hazards you might encounter when doing an investigation in the field.

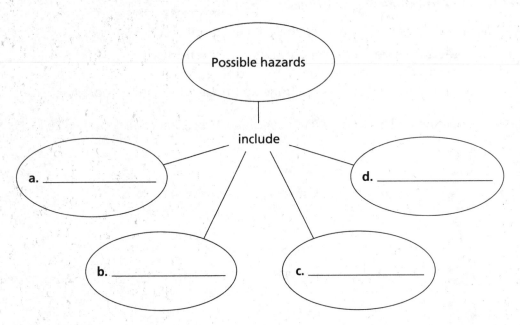

18. Circle the letter of each sentence that you should do whenever you do field work.

    a. Work alone as much as possible.

    b. Tell an adult where you will be.

    c. Ask an adult or classmate to accompany you.

In Case of an Accident (p. 26)

19. What should you do immediately whenever an accident occurs?

_____

_____

20. Circle the letter of what to do if you spill something on your skin while doing a lab.

    a. Cover the skin with a clean dressing.

    b. Wash your hands.

    c. Flush the skin with large amounts of water.

    d. Do nothing unless the skin blisters.

Waves and the Electromagnetic Spectrum

Key Concepts

- What causes waves?
- What are the basic properties of waves?
- What does an electromagnetic wave consist of?
- What are the waves of the electromagnetic spectrum?

A **wave** is a disturbance that transfers energy from place to place. In science, **energy** is defined as the ability to do work.

The material through which a wave travels is called a **medium.** Gases, liquids, and solids can all be mediums. Waves that require a medium through which to travel are called **mechanical waves. Mechanical waves are produced when a source of energy causes a medium to vibrate.** A **vibration** is a repeated back-and-forth or up-and-down motion.

All waves share certain properties. **The basic properties of waves are amplitude, wavelength, frequency, and speed.**

The high point of a wave is called a **crest,** and the low point is called a **trough. Amplitude** is the maximum distance the particles of the medium carrying the wave move away from their rest positions.

The distance between two troughs or two crests of a wave is the **wavelength.** The **frequency** of a wave is the number of complete waves that pass a given point in a certain amount of time. Frequency is measured in units called **hertz (Hz).** The speed of a wave is how far the wave travels in a given amount of time.

An **electromagnetic wave** transfers electrical and magnetic energy. It does not need a medium through which to travel. **An electromagnetic wave consists of vibrating electric and magnetic fields that move through space at the speed of light.** Light and all other electromagnetic waves are produced by charged particles. Every charged particle has an electric field surrounding it. When a charged particle moves, it produces a magnetic field. The energy that is transferred through space by electromagnetic waves is called **electromagnetic radiation.**

All electromagnetic waves travel at the same speed in a vacuum, but they have different wavelengths and different frequencies. The **electromagnetic spectrum** is the complete range of electromagnetic waves when they are placed in order of increasing frequency. **The electromagnetic spectrum is made up of radio waves, infrared rays, visible light, ultraviolet rays, X-rays, and gamma rays.** Electromagnetic waves that you can see are called **visible light.**

Radio waves are the electromagnetic waves with the longest wavelengths. Infrared rays have shorter wavelengths. Electromagnetic waves with wavelengths just shorter than those of visible light are called **ultraviolet rays.** X-rays are electromagnetic waves with very short wavelengths. Gamma rays have the shortest wavelengths.

Using Light · *Reading/Notetaking Guide*

Waves and the Electromagnetic Spectrum

(pp. 38–45)

This section explains what causes waves and describes the properties of waves and the waves of the electromagnetic spectrum.

Use Target Reading Skills

Before you read, preview Figure 2, "Amplitude, Wavelength, and Frequency." Use the graphic organizer below to ask questions about the illustration. After you read, answer your questions.

Questions	Answers

Name _____ Date _____ Class _____

Waves and Energy (p. 39)

1. What is a wave?

   _____

   _____

2. The material through which a wave travels is a(n)

   _____.

3. Circle the letter of each of the following that can act as a medium.
   a. solids
   b. liquids
   c. gases
   d. empty space

4. Waves that require a medium through which to travel are called

   _____.

5. Is the following sentence true or false? When waves travel through a medium, they carry the medium with them. _____

6. Give an example of a wave that can travel through empty space.

   _____

7. Mechanical waves are produced when a source of energy causes a medium to _____.

8. What is a vibration?

   _____

   _____

Using Light · *Reading/Notetaking Guide*

Waves and the Electromagnetic Spectrum (continued)

Properties of Waves (pp. 40–41)

9. List four properties of waves.

   a. _____

   b. _____

   c. _____

   d. _____

10. The maximum distance that the particles of the medium carrying a wave move away from their rest position is called the wave's

    _____.

11. Explain what the amplitude of a water wave is.

    _____

    _____

    _____

Using Light · *Reading/Notetaking Guide*

12. Define *crest* and *trough*.

   a. crest: _____

   b. trough: _____

13. The amplitude of a wave is a direct measure of its
    _____.

14. The distance between two corresponding parts of a wave is its
    _____.

15. How can you determine a wave's wavelength?

    _____

    _____

16. The number of complete waves that pass a given point in a certain
    amount of time is called the wave's _____.

17. If you make a wave in a rope so that one wave passes every second, what
    is its frequency?

    _____

18. Circle the letter of the unit used to measure frequency.

   a. watt

   b. second

   c. joule

   d. hertz

19. How can you determine the speed of a wave?

    _____

Using Light ▪ *Reading/Notetaking Guide*

Waves and the Electromagnetic Spectrum *(continued)*

What Is an Electromagnetic Wave? (p. 42)

20. What are electromagnetic waves?

   _____

   _____

21. Is the following sentence true or false? Electromagnetic waves can transfer energy through a medium. _____

22. What do electromagnetic waves consist of?

   _____

   _____

23. The energy that is transferred by electromagnetic waves is called

   _____.

24. Circle the letter of each sentence that is true about electric and magnetic fields.

   a. An electromagnetic wave occurs when electric and magnetic fields vibrate at right angles to each other.

   b. A magnetic field is surrounded by an electric current.

   c. When an electric field vibrates, so does the magnetic field.

   d. Every charged particle is surrounded by a magnetic field.

25. Is the following sentence true or false? All electromagnetic waves travel at the same speed in a vacuum. _____

Using Light • *Reading/Notetaking Guide*

What Is the Electromagnetic Spectrum? (pp. 43–45)

26. Circle the letter of each sentence that is true about electromagnetic waves.

    a. Different electromagnetic waves have different frequencies.
    b. All electromagnetic waves have the same wavelength.
    c. Different electromagnetic waves have different wavelengths.
    d. All electromagnetic waves travel at the same speed in a vacuum.

27. Circle the letter of each sentence that is true about electromagnetic waves.

    a. As the wavelength of electromagnetic waves decreases, the frequency increases.
    b. Waves with the longest wavelengths have the lowest frequencies.
    c. As the frequency of electromagnetic waves decreases, the wavelength increases.
    d. Waves with the shortest wavelengths have the lowest frequencies.

28. What is the name for the range of electromagnetic waves when they are placed in order of increasing frequency?

_____

29. Label the electromagnetic spectrum below with the names of the different waves that make up the spectrum.

Electromagnetic Spectrum

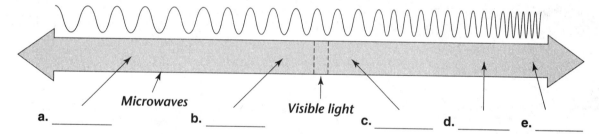

Microwaves

Visible light

a. _____ b. _____ c. _____ d. _____ e. _____

Using Light · *Reading/Notetaking Guide*

Waves and the Electromagnetic Spectrum *(continued)*

30. Which type of electromagnetic waves carry television signals?

_____

31. Is the following sentence true or false? Microwaves are the radio waves with the shortest wavelengths and highest frequencies.

_____

32. Is the following sentence true or false? Microwaves are used for cellular phone communication. _____

33. The energy you feel as heat from an electric burner is carried by electromagnetic waves called _____.

34. Circle the letter of each sentence that is true about infrared rays.

   a. Infrared rays have a higher frequency than radio waves.
   b. Infrared cameras can "see" warm objects in the dark.
   c. Infrared rays are sometimes called gamma rays.
   d. Heat lamps give off no infrared rays.

35. The part of the electromagnetic spectrum that you can see is called

_____.

36. Write the names of the colors of visible light from longest wavelength to shortest wavelength.

   a. _____ **b.** _____ **c.** _____

   d. _____ **e.** _____ **f.** _____

37. Electromagnetic waves with wavelengths just shorter than those of visible light are called _____.

38. Circle the letter of each sentence that is true about ultraviolet rays.
    a. Too much exposure to ultraviolet rays can cause skin cancer.
    b. Humans with good vision can see ultraviolet rays.
    c. Ultraviolet rays cause skin cells to produce vitamin D.
    d. Ultraviolet rays can damage or kill living cells.

39. Electromagnetic waves with frequencies higher than ultraviolet rays but lower than gamma rays are _____.

40. X-rays are used to make images of teeth and bones because

    _____.

41. The electromagnetic waves with the shortest wavelengths and the highest frequencies are called _____.

42. What have gamma rays been used for?

    _____

    _____

Chapter 2 Using Light ▪ *Section 2 Summary*

Visible Light and Color

Key Concepts

■ How does visible light interact with an object?

When light strikes an object, the light can be reflected, transmitted, or absorbed. What happens to the light depends on the type of material the object is made of. A **transparent material** transmits most of the light that strikes it. This allows you to see clearly what is on the other side. Clear glass, water, and air are transparent. A **translucent material** scatters light as it passes through. You can usually see something behind a translucent object, but the details are blurred. Wax paper and frosted glass are translucent. An **opaque material** reflects or absorbs all of the light that strikes it. You cannot see through an opaque material because light cannot pass through it. Wood and metal are opaque.

The color of an opaque object is the color of the light it reflects. An apple appears red because it reflects only red light. Opaque objects can appear to change color in a different color of light. For example, in blue light a red apple looks black, because there is no red light for the apple to reflect.

A wide range of colors can be produced using just a few basic colors. Three colors that can combine to make any other color are called **primary colors.** Two primary colors combine in equal amounts to produce a **secondary color.** The primary colors of light are red, green, and blue. The secondary colors of light are yellow (red + green), cyan (green + blue), and magenta (red + blue). **When combined in equal amounts, the three primary colors of light produce white light.** If the three primary colors of light are combined in different amounts, they can produce other colors. **Complementary colors** are a primary color and a secondary color that can combine to form white light. Blue and yellow are examples of complementary colors.

Pigments are colored substances that are used to color other materials. They include inks, paints, and dyes. The color of a pigment is the color of light that the pigment reflects. **As pigments are added together, fewer colors of light are reflected and more are absorbed.** The more pigments that are combined, the darker the mixture looks. The primary colors of pigments are cyan, yellow, and magenta. The secondary colors of pigments are red, green, and blue. The primary pigment colors combine in equal amounts to produce black. Many other colors of pigments can be produced by combining the primary pigment colors in different amounts.

Using Light • *Reading/Notetaking Guide*

Visible Light and Color (pp. 46–50)

This section explains how visible light interacts with an object.

Use Target Reading Skills

Before you read, preview Figure 8, "Primary Colors of Light." Use the graphic organizer below to ask questions about the illustration. Then, answer your questions.

Questions	Answers

Visible Light (p. 47)

1. What three things can happen when light strikes an object?

   _____

   _____

2. In which three categories can most materials be classified, based on what happens to light that strikes the material?

   _____

   _____

3. What happens to light that strikes a translucent material?

   _____

   _____

The Color of Objects (p. 48)

4. The color of an opaque object is the color of the light it

   _____.

5. Explain why you see the skin of an apple as red.

   _____

   _____

6. Is the following sentence true or false? Objects can look different in color depending on the color of light in which they are seen.

   _____

Using Light · *Reading/Notetaking Guide*

Visible Light and Color *(continued)*

7. What color does a green leaf appear to be in red light? Why?

_____

_____

Combining Colors *(pp. 49–50)*

8. The three colors that can be used to make any other color are called
_____.

9. Any two primary colors combined in equal amounts produce a(n)
_____.

10. What are the three primary colors of light?

_____

11. When combined in equal amounts, what do the three primary colors of
light produce?

_____

12. Complete the following "equations" by writing the secondary color that
the two primary colors of light produce when they are combined in
equal amounts.

   a. green + blue = _____

   b. red + green = _____

   c. red + blue = _____

13. Any two colors of light that combine to form white light are called
_____.

14. What are pigments?

_____

_____

15. Complete the following "equations" by writing the secondary color that
the two primary colors of pigments produce when they are combined.

   a. magenta + cyan = _____

   b. magenta + yellow = _____

   c. cyan + yellow = _____

Reflection and Refraction

Key Concepts

- What does the law of reflection state?

- Why do light rays bend when they enter a new medium at an angle?

- What determines the types of images formed by convex and concave lenses?

Reflection occurs when an object or wave bounces back off a surface through which it cannot pass. **The law of reflection states that the angle of incidence equals the angle of reflection.**

The reflection you see in a mirror depends on how the surface reflects light. An **image** is a copy of an object formed by reflected or refracted rays of light. A **plane mirror** is one that is flat. A plane mirror produces an image that is upright and the same size as the object being reflected. The image you see in a plane mirror is a virtual image. "Virtual" describes something that does not really exist. **Virtual images** are always right-side up, or upright.

A mirror with a surface that curves inward like the inside of a bowl is a **concave mirror.** A concave mirror can reflect parallel rays of light so that they meet at a point. The point at which the rays meet is called the **focal point.** It lies on the **optical axis,** which is an imaginary line that divides a mirror in half. Concave mirrors can form either virtual images or real images. If the object is farther away from the mirror than the focal point, the reflected rays form a real image. A **real image** forms when reflected rays actually meet. Real images are upside down. If the object is between the mirror and the focal point, the reflected rays form a virtual image. The image appears to be behind the mirror. The image is upright and larger than the object.

A mirror with a surface that curves outward is called a **convex mirror.** The rays spread out but appear to come from a focal point behind the mirror. Because the rays never meet, the images formed by convex mirrors are always virtual and smaller than the object. Because they are smaller, the images appear to be farther away than they actually are.

As light passes from one medium to another, it refracts. **When light rays enter a new medium at an angle, the change in speed causes them to bend, or change direction.** When light passes from air into water, the light slows down. When light passes from glass into the air, the light speeds up. Light travels faster in air, a little slower in water, and still slower in glass.

A **lens** is a curved piece of glass or other transparent material that is used to refract light. A **convex lens** is thicker in the center than at the edges. A convex lens bends parallel light rays toward the center of the lens. **An object's position relative to the focal point determines whether a convex lens forms a real image or a virtual image.** A **concave lens** is thinner in the center than at the edges. A concave lens spreads out parallel rays of light. **A concave lens can produce only virtual images because parallel light rays passing through the lens never meet.**

Using Light · *Reading/Notetaking Guide*

Reflection and Refraction (pp. 52–60)

This section explains the law of reflection, discusses why light rays bend when entering a new medium, and presents the types of images formed by convex and concave lenses.

Use Target Reading Skills

As you read, compare and contrast concave and convex mirrors in a Venn diagram like the one below. Write the similarities in the space where the circles overlap and the differences on the left and right sides.

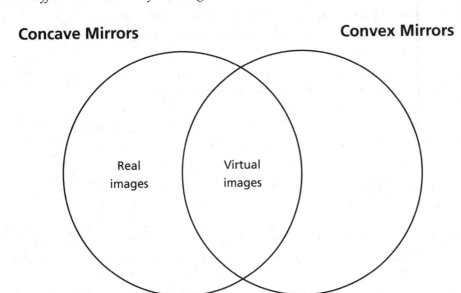

Concave Mirrors   **Convex Mirrors**

Real images   Virtual images

Reflection (p. 53)

1. Is the following sentence true or false? The reflection you see in a mirror depends on how the surface reflects light._____

2. What is the law of reflection?

   _____

   _____

3. The interaction of light beams with a surface is called

   _____.

Mirrors (pp. 54–56)

4. What is a plane mirror?

   _____

   _____

   _____

5. A copy of an object formed by reflected or retracted rays of light is called a(n) _____

Using Light · *Reading/Notetaking Guide*

6. What is a virtual image?

_____

_____

7. What size of image does a plane mirror produce?

_____

8. How does the image in a plane mirror differ from the object?

_____

_____

9. A mirror with a surface that curves inward like the inside of a bowl is
a(n) _____.

10. Is the following sentence true or false? The optical axis is an imaginary
line that divides a mirror. _____

11. The point at which light rays meet is called the
_____.

12. What type(s) of image can concave mirrors form?

_____

_____

13. An image formed when rays actually meet is called a(n)
_____.

14. Complete the table about kinds of mirrors.

Kinds of Mirrors			
Kind of Mirror	**Description**	**Virtual or Real Image?**	**Upright or Inverted?**
a.	Flat	b.	c.
d.	Curved inward	Virtual or real	Inverted or upright
e.	Curved outward	f.	Upright

15. Why are objects in a car mirror closer than they appear?

_____

_____

Reflection and Refraction *(continued)*

Refraction (pp. 57–58)

16. When light rays enter a new medium at an angle, what does the change in speed cause the rays to do?

   _____

   _____

17. Rank the following mediums according to how fast light travels through them. Rank the fastest as *1*.

   _____ **a.** water   _____ **b.** glass   _____ **c.** air

18. Why does a prism cause white light to separate into the colors of the spectrum?

   _____

   _____

Lenses (pp. 59–60)

19. A curved piece of glass or other transparent material that is used to refract light is called a(n) _____.

20. How does a lens form an image?

   _____

   _____

Using Light • *Reading/Notetaking Guide*

21. Label each lens as either a convex lens or a concave lens. Then draw light rays to show how light is refracted as it passes through each lens.

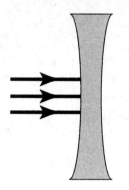

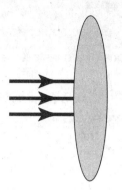

a. _____   b. _____

22. Complete the following table about lenses.

Kinds of Lenses		
Kind of Lens	**Description of Lens**	**Image Formed—Real or Virtual?**
a.	Thinner at the center than at the edges	**b.**
Convex	**c.**	Real or virtual

23. What two factors determine the type of image formed by a lens?

_____

_____

24. An object's position relative to the _____ determines whether a convex lens forms a real or virtual image.

25. Why can a concave lens produce only virtual images?

_____

_____

26. Is the following sentence true or false? The image formed by a concave lens is always upright and smaller than the object._____

Chapter 2 Using Light · *Section 4 Summary*

Seeing Light

Key Concepts

- How do you see objects?
- What types of lenses are used to correct vision problems?

Your eyes allow you to sense light. **When light from an object enters your eye, your eye sends a signal to your brain and you see the object.** Light enters the eye through the transparent front surface called the cornea. Then light enters the pupil, the part of the eye that looks black. The **pupil** is an opening through which light enters the inside of the eye. In dim light, the pupil becomes larger to allow in more light. In bright light, the pupil becomes smaller to allow in less light. The **iris** is a ring of muscle that contracts and expands to change the size of the pupil.

After entering the pupil, light passes through the lens. The lens bends light to form an upside-down image on the retina. The **retina** is a layer of cells that line the inside of the eyeball. The retina is made up of tiny light-sensitive cells called rods and cones. **Rods** contain a pigment that responds to small amounts of light. **Cones** respond to color. They may detect red light, green light, or blue light. Cones respond best in bright light. Both rods and cones help change images on the retina into signals that then travel to the brain along the optic nerve.

If the eyeball is slightly too long or too short, the image on the retina is out of focus. Wearing glasses or contact lenses can correct this type of vision problem. **Concave lenses are used to correct nearsightedness. Convex lenses are used to correct farsightedness.**

A **nearsighted** person can see nearby objects clearly, but distant objects are blurred. The eyeball is too long, so the image forms in front of the retina. A concave lens bends light rays outward before they enter the eye. This causes the image to focus on the retina as it should.

A **farsighted** person can see distant objects clearly, but nearby objects are blurred. The eyeball is too short, so the image that falls on the retina is out of focus. A convex lens bends the light rays inward before they enter the eye, so the image focuses on the retina.

Using Light · *Reading/Notetaking Guide*

Seeing Light (pp. 62–64)

This section explains how you see light and what types of lenses are used to correct vision problems.

Use Target Reading Skills

As you read, complete the outline by adding important details. Use the headings and Key Terms to help you complete the outline.

I. Vision
   A.
   B.
   C.
   D.
   E.
   F.
II. Correcting Vision
   A.
   B.
   C.

Vision (p. 63)

Match the part of the eye with its description.

Part of Eye	Description
____ **1.** Cornea	**a.** hole through which light enters the eye
____ **2.** Iris	**b.** transparent front surface of the eye
____ **3.** Pupil	**c.** short, thick nerve through which signals travel to the brain from the eye
____ **4.** Lens	**d.** ring of muscle around the pupil
____ **5.** Retina	**e.** curved part of the eye behind the pupil, that refracts light
____ **6.** Optic nerve	**f.** layer of cells lining the inside of the eyeball

Using Light · *Reading/Notetaking Guide*

Seeing Light (continued)

7. Label the parts of the eye on the illustration.

a. _____

b. _____

c. _____

d. _____

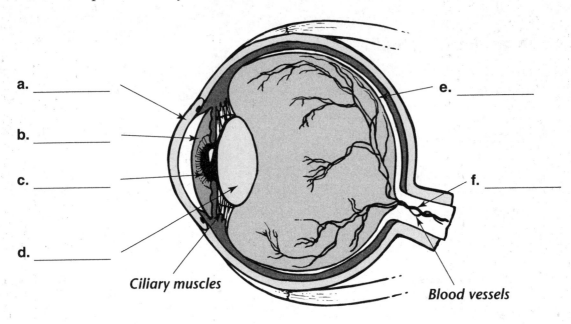

e. _____

f. _____

Ciliary muscles

Blood vessels

Correcting Vision (p. 64)

8. List the type of lenses used to correct nearsightedness and farsightedness.

a. nearsightedness: _____

b. farsightedness: _____

9. Why can't a nearsighted person clearly see objects that are far away?

_____

_____

10. Why can't a farsighted person clearly see objects that are nearby?

_____

_____

Chapter 2 Using Light · *Section 5 Summary*

Optical Tools

Key Concepts

■ How are lenses used in cameras, telescopes, and microscopes?

Three common types of optical instruments are telescopes, microscopes, and cameras. Cameras allow scientists to record photographs of the objects they see. Telescopes help them see objects that are very far away. And microscopes help them see tiny objects by magnifying them.

A **camera** uses one or more lenses to focus light. It records images on film. Light from an object travels to the camera and passes through the lens. **The lens of the camera focuses light to form a real, upside-down image on film in the back of the camera.**

A **telescope** forms enlarged images of distant objects. **Telescopes use combinations of lenses or mirrors to collect and focus light from distant objects.** The most common use of telescopes is to study objects in space.

The two main types of telescopes are refracting telescopes and reflecting telescopes. A **refracting telescope** consists of two convex lenses, one at each end of a long tube. The larger lens is called the objective. The **objective** gathers the light coming from an object. It focuses the rays to form a real image. The lens close to your eye is called the eyepiece. The **eyepiece** magnifies the image so you can see it clearly.

A **reflecting telescope** uses a large concave mirror to gather light. The mirror collects light from distant objects and focuses the rays to form a real image. A small mirror inside the telescope reflects the image to the eyepiece. The images you see through the telescope are upside down.

A **microscope** is an optical tool that forms enlarged images of tiny objects. **A microscope uses a combination of lenses to form enlarged images of tiny objects.** For a microscope to be useful, it must combine two important properties—magnification and resolution.

The lenses in light microscopes magnify an object by bending the light that passes through them. Since light microscopes have more than one lens, they are also called compound microscopes. Light passes through a specimen and then through two lenses. The first lens, the objective, magnifies the object. Then a second lens, the eyepiece, further magnifies the enlarged image. The total magnification of the microscope is equal to the magnifications of the two lenses multiplied together.

In the 1930s, scientists developed the electron microscope. The **electron microscope** uses a beam of electrons instead of light to produce a magnified image. Electron microscopes can obtain pictures of extremely small objects— much smaller than those that can be seen with light microscopes. The resolution of electron microscopes is much better than the resolution of light microscopes.

Using Light • *Reading/Notetaking Guide*

Optical Tools (pp. 65–69)

This section describes how lenses are used in cameras, telescopes, and microscopes.

Use Target Reading Skills

Before you read, preview Figure 24, "A Compound Microscope." Use the graphic organizer below to ask questions about the illustration. Then, answer your questions.

Questions	Answers

Cameras (p. 66)

1. What is a camera?

   _____

2. What is the function of the lens in a camera?

   _____

   _____

3. Opening the shutter allows _____ passing through the _____ to hit the film.

4. Is the following sentence true or false? The diaphragm of a camera controls the amount of light hitting the film, which is similar to how the iris controls the pupil in the human eye. _____

Using Light · *Reading/Notetaking Guide*

Telescopes (p. 67)

5. An optical instrument that forms enlarged images of distant objects is called a(n) _____.

6. Complete the table about telescopes.

Types of Telescopes	
Type of Telescope	**Lenses or Mirrors?**
a.	b. _____ lenses
c.	d. _____ mirrors

7. What does the objective of a refracting telescope do?

_____

_____

8. What does the eyepiece of a refracting telescope do?

_____

_____

9. The images you see through a reflecting telescope are _____ and _____.

Microscopes (pp. 68–69)

10. An optical instrument that forms enlarged images of tiny objects is called a(n) _____.

Discovering Cells

Key Concepts

- What are cells?

- How did the invention of the microscope contribute to knowledge about living things?

- What is the cell theory?

- How are the cells of multicellular organisms organized?

All living things are made of **cells. Cells are the basic units of structure and function in living things.** Cells carry out the basic processes of life in similar ways. Most cells are too small to be seen with the naked eye.

The invention of the microscope made it possible for people to discover and learn about cells. One of the first people to observe cells was Robert Hooke. In 1663, Hooke observed the structure of a thin slice of cork using a compound microscope he had built himself. He saw millions of empty spaces he called *cells*. At about the same time, Anton van Leeuwenhoek built simple microscopes and used them to observe tiny objects. Leeuwenhoek observed a variety of moving one-celled organisms and called them *animalcules*.

In 1838, Matthias Schleiden concluded that all plants are made of cells. The next year, Theodor Schwann concluded that all animals are also made of cells. In 1855, Rudolf Virchow proposed that new cells are formed only from existing cells. Schleiden, Schwann, Virchow, and others helped develop the **cell theory. The cell theory states: All living things are composed of cells; cells are the basic unit of structure and function in living things; all cells are produced from other cells.** Because cells come from other cells, scientists can study cells to learn about growth and reproduction.

Organisms may be composed of only one cell or many trillions of cells. **Unicellular** organisms, such as bacteria, are made up of only one cell. **Multicellular** organisms are composed of many cells.

In multicellular organisms, cells are often organized into tissues, organs, and organ systems. A **tissue** is a group of similar cells that work together to perform a specific function. An **organ** is made up of different kinds of tissues that work together. An **organ system,** such as the nervous system, is a group of organs that work together to perform a major function.

Cell Structure and Function • *Reading/Notetaking Guide*

Discovering Cells (pp. 80–85)

This section describes what cells are and how the invention of the microscope led to the development of a theory on cells. The section also explains how cells of multicellular organisms are organized.

Use Target Reading Skills

As you read, construct a flowchart showing how the work of Hooke, Leeuwenhoek, Schleiden, Schwann, and Virchow contributed to scientific understanding of cells.

Discovering Cells

Hooke sees cells in cork.

↓

↓

↓

↓

An Overview of Cells (p. 81)

1. What are cells?

_____

_____

Cell Structure and Function • *Reading/Notetaking Guide*

First Observations of Cells (pp. 81–83)

2. What did the invention of the microscope make possible?

   _____

   _____

3. An instrument that makes small objects look larger is a(n)

   _____.

4. Complete the following table about the first people to observe cells.

The First People to Observe Cells		
Questions	**Robert Hooke**	**Anton van Leeuwenhoek**
What did he first look at with the microscope?		
What did he discover?		

Development of the Cell Theory (pp. 84–85)

5. Is the following sentence true or false? Theodor Schwann used only his own research to develop the cell theory. _____

6. List the three points of the cell theory.

   a. _____

   b. _____

   c. _____

7. What information can scientists learn from studying cells?

   _____

   _____

Cell Structure and Function • *Reading/Notetaking Guide*

Discovering Cells *(continued)*

Unicellular and Multicellular (p. 85)

8. What are unicellular and multicellular organisms?

    _____

    _____

9. How are cells organized in most multicellular organisms?

    _____

    _____

10. A(n) _____ is a group of similar cells that work together to perform a specific function.

11. What is an organ?

    _____

12. Your brain is a(n) _____, and it is part of your nervous system, which is a(n) _____.

Looking Inside Cells

Key Concepts

- What roles do the cell wall and cell membrane play in the cell?
- What is the role of the nucleus in the cell?
- What organelles are found in the cytoplasm and what are their functions?
- How do cells differ?

A cell is very small. Inside a cell are even smaller structures called **organelles,** which carry out specific functions within the cell. The **cell wall** is a rigid layer of nonliving material that surrounds the cells of plants and some other organisms. **A cell wall helps to protect and support the cell.** The cell wall is made of a strong, flexible material called cellulose, and many materials can pass through it. Animals and many single-celled organisms do not have cell walls.

In cells that do not have cell walls, the **cell membrane** is the outside boundary that separates the cell from its environment. All cells have cell membranes. In cells with cell walls, the cell membrane is located just inside the cell wall. **The cell membrane controls what substances come into and out of a cell.**

The **nucleus** is a large, oval structure that acts as the "brain" of the cell. **The nucleus is the cell's control center, directing all of the cell's activities.** The nucleus is surrounded by a protective membrane called the nuclear envelope. Materials pass in and out of the nucleus through pores in the nuclear envelope. Inside the nucleus, strands of chromatin contain genetic material. Also, the nucleolus is the place where ribosomes are made.

The **cytoplasm** is the region between the cell membrane and the nucleus. **In the cytoplasm are many organelles, including mitochondria, the endoplasmic reticulum, ribosomes, Golgi bodies, chloroplasts, vacuoles, and lysosomes. Each of these organelles has specific functions in the cell.** The **mitochondria** are known as the "powerhouses" of the cell because they convert energy in food molecules to energy the cell can use to carry out its functions. Passageways called the **endoplasmic reticulum** carry proteins and other materials from one part of the cell to another. Small, grainlike bodies called **ribosomes** function as factories to produce proteins. Collections of sacs and tubes called **Golgi bodies** receive proteins and other newly formed materials from the endoplasmic reticulum, package them, and distribute them to other parts of the cell. The Golgi bodies release materials outside the cell. In plants and some other organisms, large, green structures called **chloroplasts** capture energy from sunlight and use it to produce food for the cell. Large water-filled sacs called **vacuoles** are the storage areas of cells. A vacuole stores food and other materials needed by the cell. Small, round structures called **lysosomes** contain chemicals that break down certain materials in the cell.

There is a lot of variety in cells—both within individual organisms and across different organisms. **The variety of structures in cells reflects differences in cell function.** Cells come in many shapes, can vary in their organelles, and may have more of a particular kind of organelle.

Cell Structure and Function ▪ *Reading/Notetaking Guide*

Looking Inside Cells (pp. 88–95)

This section describes cell structure and function in plant cells and animal cells, and explains how cells differ.

Use Target Reading Skills

Before you read, preview the figure Plant and Animal Cells *in your textbook. Then write two questions that you have about the illustrations in a graphic organizer like the one below. As you read, answer your questions.*

Plant and Animal Cells

Q. How are animal cells different from plant cells?
A.
Q.
A.

Introduction (p. 88)

1. What are organelles?

_____

_____

Enter the Cell (pp. 89–91)

2. The rigid layer of nonliving material that surrounds plant cells is the

_____.

Cell Structure and Function · *Reading/Notetaking Guide*

3. Circle the letter of each sentence that is true about the cell wall.

   a. Cell walls are made of cellulose.

   b. Plant cells have cell walls.

   c. Animal cells have cell walls.

   d. Water and oxygen cannot pass through the cell wall.

4. What does the cell wall do?

   _____

5. Where is the cell membrane located in cells that have cell walls?

   _____

6. Where is the cell membrane located in cells that do NOT have cell walls?

   _____

   _____

7. Is the following sentence true or false? The main function of the cell membrane is to control what comes into and out of a cell.

   _____

Sail On to the Nucleus (p. 92)

8. Circle the letter of each sentence that is true about the nucleus.

   a. Materials pass in and out of the nucleus through pores in the nuclear envelope.

   b. Chromatin contains the instructions that direct the functions of a cell.

   c. The nucleolus is part of the nuclear envelope.

   d. Ribosomes are made in the nucleolus.

Organelles in the Cytoplasm (pp. 93–94)

9. Circle the letter of the part of the cell that is the region between the cell membrane and the nucleus.

   a. organelle

   b. nucleus

   c. cytoplasm

   d. chromatin

Cell Structure and Function ▪ *Reading/Notetaking Guide*

Looking Inside Cells (continued)

10. In the table below, describe the function of each organelle in the cytoplasm.

Organelles in Cytoplasm	
Organelle	**Function**
Mitochondria	
Endoplasmic reticulum	
Ribosomes	
Golgi bodies	
Chloroplasts	
Vacuoles	
Lysosomes	

Cell Diversity (p. 95)

11. In a many-celled organism, cells are specialized to perform different

_____ .

12. Circle the letter of each sentence that is true about cells.
    a. All cells are the same shape.
    b. Some cells contain certain organelles but not others.
    c. Cells can have more of a particular kind of organelle.
    d. Nerve cells and red blood cells have different shapes that enable them to carry out their different functions.

Chemical Compounds in Cells

Key Concepts

- What are elements and compounds?
- How is water important to the function of cells?
- What are the functions of carbohydrates, lipids, proteins, and nucleic acids?

An element is any substance that cannot be broken down into simpler substances. The smallest unit of an **element** is called an atom. The elements found in living things include carbon, hydrogen, oxygen, nitrogen, phosphorus, and sulfur. **When two or more elements combine chemically, they form a compound.** The smallest unit of many **compounds** is called a molecule.

Water is a compound made up of hydrogen and oxygen. **Most chemical reactions within cells could not take place without water.** Water also helps cells keep their size and shape and keeps the temperature of cells from changing rapidly.

Many of the compounds in living things contain the element carbon. Most compounds that contain carbon are called organic compounds. **Carbohydrates, lipids, proteins, and nucleic acids are important groups of organic compounds in living things.** Compounds that do not contain the element carbon are called inorganic compounds.

A **carbohydrate** is an energy-rich organic compound made of the elements carbon, hydrogen, and oxygen. Sugars and starches are examples of carbohydrates. **In addition to providing energy for the cell, carbohydrates are important components of some cell parts.**

Fats, oils, and waxes are all **lipids.** Lipids are energy-rich organic compounds made of carbon, hydrogen, and oxygen. Cells store energy in lipids for later use. **In addition to their function as an energy source, lipids also make up most of the cell membrane.**

Proteins are large organic molecules made of carbon, hydrogen, oxygen, nitrogen, and, in some cases, sulfur. Protein molecules are made up of smaller molecules called **amino acids.** Proteins make up much of the structure of cells. **The proteins known as enzymes perform important functions in the chemical reactions that take place in cells.** Without **enzymes,** many chemical reactions that are necessary for life would either take too long or not occur at all.

Nucleic acids are very long organic molecules made of carbon, oxygen, hydrogen, nitrogen, and phosphorus. **Nucleic acids contain the instructions that cells need to carry out all the functions of life.** There are two kinds of nucleic acids: DNA and RNA. Deoxyribonucleic acid, or **DNA,** is the genetic material that carries information about an organism that is passed from parent to offspring and directs all of the cell's functions. Ribonucleic acid, or **RNA,** plays an important role in the production of proteins. RNA is found in the cytoplasm as well as in the nucleus.

Name _____ Date _____ Class _____

Chemical Compounds in Cells (pp. 97–101)

This section identifies the basic building blocks of cells. It also explains the importance of water to cells.

Use Target Reading Skills

As you read, write the main idea—the biggest or most important idea—in the graphic organizer below. Then write four supporting details that further explain the main idea.

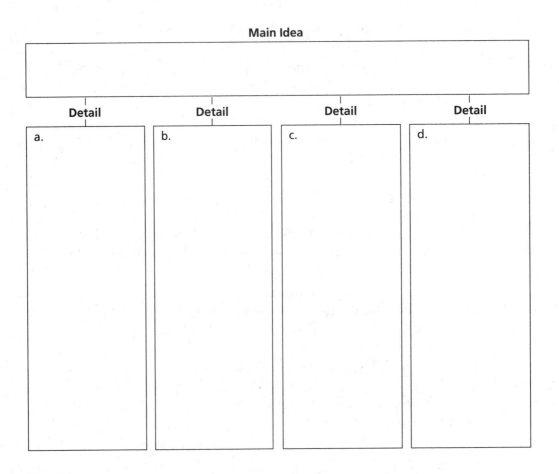

Main Idea

Detail	Detail	Detail	Detail
a.	b.	c.	d.

Elements and Compounds (pp. 97–98)

1. A(n) _____ is any substance that cannot be broken down into simpler substances. Its smallest unit is the

   _____.

2. When two or more elements combine chemically, they form a(n) _____. Its smallest unit is usually called a(n)

   _____.

3. Most chemical reactions within cells could not take place without_____.

Cell Structure and Function ▪ *Reading/Notetaking Guide*

4. Complete this concept map on organic compounds.

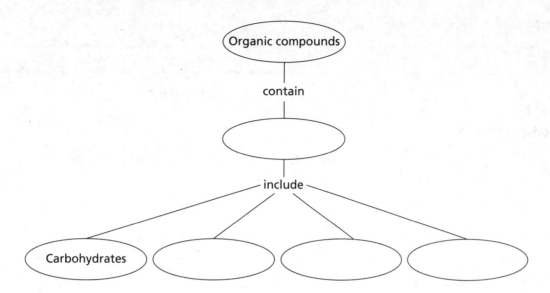

5. Compounds that do not contain carbon are called _____.

Carbohydrates (p. 99)

6. A carbohydrate is made of carbon, hydrogen, and
_____.

7. Starch is a kind of carbohydrate. What foods have starch?

_____

_____

_____

8. How do cells use carbohydrates?

_____

_____

_____

Lipids (p. 99)

9. What are three examples of lipids?

    a. _____

    b. _____

    c. _____

Cell Structure and Function ▪ *Reading/Notetaking Guide*

Chemical Compounds in Cells *(continued)*

10. How are lipids like carbohydrates?

_____

_____

11. Cells store _____ in lipids to use later.

Proteins (p. 100)

12. _____ form parts of cell membranes and many of the cell's organelles.

13. What small molecules make up proteins? _____

14. What do enzymes do?

_____

_____

Nucleic Acids (p. 101)

15. What are nucleic acids?

_____

_____

16. Is the following sentence true or false? Cells use the instructions in nucleic acids to carry out all life functions. _____

17. List the two kinds of nucleic acids.

a. _____   b. _____

Chapter 3 Cell Structure and Function • *Section 4 Summary*

The Cell in Its Environment

Key Concepts

- How do most small molecules cross the cell membrane?
- Why is osmosis important to cells?
- What is the difference between passive transport and active transport?

The cell membrane is **selectively permeable,** which means that some substances can pass through it while others cannot. Oxygen, food molecules, and waste products all must pass through the cell membrane. Substances that can move into and out of a cell do so by one of three methods: diffusion, osmosis, or active transport.

Diffusion is the main method by which small molecules move across the cell membrane. Diffusion is the process by which molecules move from an area of higher concentration to an area of lower concentration. The concentration of a substance is the amount of the substance in a given volume. Diffusion is caused by molecules moving and colliding. The collisions cause the molecules to push away from one another and spread out. Molecules diffuse through the cell membrane into a cell when there is a higher concentration of the molecules outside the cell than inside the cell.

The diffusion of water molecules through a selectively permeable membrane is called **osmosis. Because cells cannot function properly without adequate water, many cellular processes depend on osmosis.** In osmosis, water molecules move by diffusion from an area where they are highly concentrated through the cell membrane to an area where they are less concentrated.

The movement of dissolved materials through a cell membrane without using cellular energy is called **passive transport.** Diffusion and osmosis are both types of passive transport. When a cell needs to take in materials that are in higher concentration inside the cell than outside the cell, the movement of the materials requires energy. **Active transport** is the movement of materials through a cell membrane using cellular energy. The main difference between passive transport and active transport is that **active transport requires the cell to use its own energy, while passive transport does not.** Cells have several ways of moving materials by active transport. In one method, transport proteins in the cell membrane "pick up" molecules outside the cell and carry them in. Another method of active transport is engulfing, in which the cell membrane wraps around, or engulfs, a particle and forms a vacuole within the cell.

Most cells are very small. One reason is related to the fact that all materials move into and out of cells through the cell membrane. Once a molecule enters a cell, it is carried to its destination by a stream of moving cytoplasm. In a very large cell, streams of cytoplasm must travel farther to carry materials from the cell membrane to all parts of the cell.

Cell Structure and Function ▪ *Reading/Notetaking Guide*

The Cell in Its Environment (pp. 102–107)

This section tells how substances move into and out of cells.

Use Target Reading Skills

As you read, write the main idea—the biggest or most important idea—in the graphic organizer below. Then write three supporting details that further explain the main idea.

Main Idea

Detail a.	**Detail** b.	**Detail** c.

Introduction (pp. 102–103)

1. The cell membrane is _____, which means that some substances can pass through it while others cannot.

Diffusion (pp. 103–104)

2. List three ways that substances can move into and out of a cell.

   a. _____

   b. _____

   c. _____

3. In diffusion, molecules move from an area of _____ concentration to an area of _____ concentration.

Cell Structure and Function ▪ *Reading/Notetaking Guide*

4. Draw molecules on Part B of the diagram below to show how the molecules are distributed inside and outside the cell after diffusion has occurred.

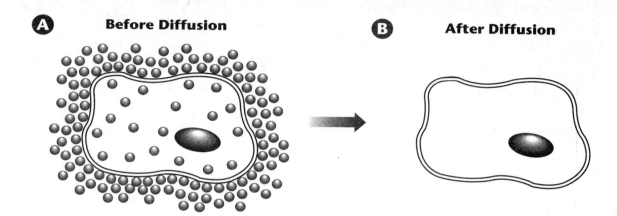

Osmosis (pp. 104–105)

5. What is osmosis?

    _____

    _____

6. Why do many cellular processes depend on osmosis?

    _____

Active Transport (pp. 106–107)

7. Two ways of moving things into and out of cells that do NOT need energy are _____ and _____.
   Moving materials through a cell membrane without using energy is called _____ transport.

8. How does active transport differ from passive transport?

    _____

    _____

    _____

9. List two ways that the cell moves things by active transport.

    a. _____

    b. _____

10. Is the following sentence true or false? As a cell gets larger, it takes longer for a molecule that has entered the cell to reach the middle of the cell.

    _____

Chapter 4 Cell Processes and Energy ▪ *Section 1 Summary*

Photosynthesis

Key Concepts

- How does the sun supply living things with the energy they need?
- What happens during the process of photosynthesis?

The sun is the source of energy for most living things. All cells need energy to carry out their functions. The process by which a cell captures the energy in sunlight and uses it to make food is called **photosynthesis.**

Nearly all living things obtain energy either directly or indirectly from the energy of sunlight captured during photosynthesis. Plants, such as grass, use energy from the sun to make their own food through the process of photosynthesis. An organism that makes its own food is called an **autotroph.** An organism that cannot make its own food is called a **heterotroph.** Many heterotrophs obtain food by eating other organisms.

Photosynthesis is a complex process. **During photosynthesis, plants and some other organisms use energy from the sun to convert carbon dioxide and water into oxygen and sugars.** Photosynthesis takes place in two stages: (1) capturing the sun's energy and (2) producing sugars. In plants, this energy-capturing process occurs mostly in the leaves. The chloroplasts in plant cells give plants their green color. The green color comes from **pigments,** colored chemical compounds that absorb light. The main photosynthetic pigment in chloroplasts is **chlorophyll.** Chlorophyll captures light energy and uses it to power the second stage of photosynthesis to produce sugars. The cell needs two raw materials for this stage: water (H_2O) and carbon dioxide (CO_2). Plant roots absorb water from the soil, and the water then moves up to the leaves. Carbon dioxide enters the plant through small openings on the undersides of the leaves called **stomata.** Once in the leaves, the water and carbon dioxide move into the chloroplasts.

Inside the chloroplasts, the water and carbon dioxide undergo a complex series of chemical reactions and produce two important products of photosynthesis: sugar and oxygen. Plant cells use sugar for food and to make other compounds, such as cellulose. Plant cells also store sugar for later use. Oxygen exits the leaf through the stomata. Almost all of the oxygen in Earth's atmosphere was produced by living things through photosynthesis. The events of photosynthesis can be summed up by the following chemical equation:

$$\overset{\text{light energy}}{6\,CO_2 \quad + \quad 6\,H_2O \quad \rightarrow \quad C_6H_{12}O_6 \quad + \quad 6\,O_2}$$

$$\underset{\text{carbon dioxide}}{} \qquad \underset{\text{water}}{} \qquad \underset{\text{a sugar}}{} \qquad \underset{\text{oxygen}}{}$$

Name _____ Date _____ Class _____

Cell Processes and Energy • *Reading/Notetaking Guide*

Photosynthesis (pp. 116–120)

This section explains how plants make food by using the energy from sunlight.

Use Target Reading Skills

As you read, make an outline to show the relationships between main ideas and supporting ideas. Use the headings, subheadings, Key Terms, and Key Concepts to help you complete the outline.

I. Sources of Energy
  A.
  B.
  C.
  D.
  E.

II.
  A.
    1.
    2.
    3.
  B.
    1.
    2.
    3.
    4.
    5.
    6.
  C.
    1.
    2.

Sources of Energy (p. 117)

1. In the process of photosynthesis, plants use the energy in _____ to make food.

Cell Processes and Energy

© Pearson Education, Inc., publishing as Pearson Prentice Hall. All rights reserved.

69

Cell Processes and Energy ▪ *Reading/Notetaking Guide*

Photosynthesis *(continued)*

2. Complete the following table about how living things use the sun's energy.

How Living Things Obtain Energy From the Sun		
Living Thing	**Autotroph or Heterotroph?**	**Obtains Energy From the Sun Directly or Indirectly?**
Grass		
Zebra		
Lion		

The Two Stages of Photosynthesis (pp. 118–120)

3. List the two stages in the process of photosynthesis.

   a. _____

   b. _____

4. The green pigment in chloroplasts, called _____, absorbs light energy from the sun.

5. Is the following sentence true or false? Besides the energy in sunlight, the cell needs water and carbon dioxide to make sugar. _____

6. What are stomata?

   _____

   _____

7. Circle the letter of each product of photosynthesis.

   a. water

   b. carbon dioxide

   c. oxygen

   d. sugars

8. Is the following sentence true or false? Photosynthesis produces the carbon dioxide that most living things need to survive. _____

9. Write the chemical equation for the process of photosynthesis.

   _____

10. What word does the arrow in the chemical equation stand for?

   _____

11. Circle the letter of each raw material of photosynthesis.

   a. carbon dioxide

   b. glucose

   c. water

   d. oxygen

12. Circle the letter of each sentence that is true about the products of photosynthesis.

   a. Plant cells use the sugar for food.

   b. Some of the sugar is made into other compounds, such as cellulose.

   c. Some of the sugar is stored in the plant's cells for later use.

   d. Extra sugar molecules pass out of the plant through the stomata.

Respiration

Key Concepts

- What events occur during respiration?

- What is fermentation?

Cells store and use energy in a way that is similar to the way you deposit and withdraw money from a savings account. When you eat a meal, you add to your body's energy savings account. When your cells need energy, they make a withdrawal by breaking down the carbohydrates in food to release energy.

The process by which cells obtain energy from glucose (a type of sugar) is called **respiration. During respiration, cells break down simple food molecules such as sugar and release the energy they contain.** Because living things need a continuous supply of energy, the cells of all living things carry out respiration continuously. The term *respiration* also is used to mean breathing, that is, moving air in and out of your lungs. To avoid confusion, the respiration process that takes place inside cells sometimes is called cellular respiration. The two kinds of respiration are related. Breathing brings oxygen into your lungs, and oxygen is necessary for cellular respiration to occur in most cells.

Like photosynthesis, respiration is a two-stage process. The first stage takes place in the cytoplasm of the organism's cells. There, glucose molecules are broken down into smaller molecules. Oxygen is not involved in this stage of respiration, and only a small amount of energy is released. The second stage of respiration takes place in the mitochondria. There, the small molecules are broken down into even smaller molecules. These chemical reactions require oxygen, and a great deal of energy is released. Two other products of respiration are carbon dioxide and water.

Photosynthesis and respiration can be thought of as opposite processes. Together, these two processes form a cycle that keeps the levels of oxygen and carbon dioxide fairly constant in the atmosphere.

Some cells obtain their energy through **fermentation**, an energy-releasing process that does not require oxygen. **Fermentation provides energy for cells without using oxygen.** One type of fermentation occurs in yeast and some other single-celled organisms. This process is sometimes called alcoholic fermentation because alcohol is one of the products made when these organisms break down sugars. Another type of fermentation takes place at times in your body when your muscles run out of oxygen—for example, when you've run as fast as you could for as long as you could. One product of this type of fermentation is an acid known as lactic acid. When lactic acid builds up, your muscles feel weak and sore.

Cell Processes and Energy • *Reading/Notetaking Guide*

Respiration (pp. 121–125)

In this section, you will learn how cells get energy from food.

Use Target Reading Skills

As you read, make an outline to show the relationships between main ideas and supporting ideas. Use the headings, subheadings, Key Terms, and Key Concepts to help you complete the outline.

I. What Is Respiration?
  A.
  B.
  C.
  D.
  E.
  F.
  G.
  H.

II.
  A.
  B.
  C.

What Is Respiration? (pp. 122–124)

1. What happens during respiration?

   _____

   _____

   _____

   _____

2. Cells store energy in the form of _____.

Cell Processes and Energy • *Reading/Notetaking Guide*

Respiration *(continued)*

3. How do cells "withdraw" energy?

_____

_____

4. Is the following sentence true or false? Respiration that takes place inside of cells is the same as breathing air in and out of the lungs.

_____

5. Use the table below to list the raw materials and products of respiration.

Respiration	
Raw Materials	**Products**

Match the events in respiration with the stages in which they occur. The items in the second column may be used more than once.

Event in Respiration	Stage of Process
_____ 6. Takes place in the mitochondria	a. first stage only
_____ 7. Takes place in the cytoplasm	b. second stage only
_____ 8. Oxygen is involved.	c. both first and second stages
_____ 9. Energy is released.	
_____ 10. Glucose molecules are broken down.	

Cell Processes and Energy · *Reading/Notetaking Guide*

11. Complete the cycle diagram below, which describes the relationship between photosynthesis and respiration.

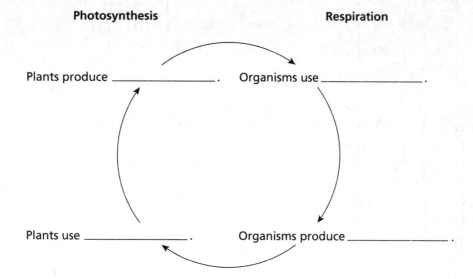

Photosynthesis   **Respiration**

Plants produce _____ .   Organisms use _____ .

Plants use _____ .   Organisms produce _____ .

Fermentation (pp. 124–125)

12. What is fermentation?

_____

_____

13. Is the following sentence true or false? Fermentation releases more energy than respiration. _____

14. List the two types of fermentation and explain where each takes place.

a. _____

_____

b. _____

_____

Cell Division

Key Concepts

- What events take place during the three stages of the cell cycle?

- How does the structure of DNA help account for the way in which DNA copies itself?

The regular sequence of growth and division that cells undergo is known as the **cell cycle**. The cell cycle is divided into three main stages.

The first stage of the cell cycle is called **interphase**. **During interphase, the cell grows, makes a copy of its DNA, and prepares to divide into two cells.** During the first part of interphase, the cell grows to full size and produces all the structures it needs. In the next part of interphase, the cell makes an exact copy of the DNA in its nucleus in a process called **replication**. At the end of DNA replication, the cell contains two identical sets of DNA.

Once interphase is complete, the second stage of the cell cycle begins. **Mitosis** is the stage during which the cell's nucleus divides into two new nuclei. **During mitosis, one copy of the DNA is distributed into each of the two daughter cells.** Scientists divide mitosis into four parts, or phases: prophase, metaphase, anaphase, and telophase. During prophase, the threadlike chromatin in the cell's nucleus condenses to form double-rod structures called **chromosomes**. Each identical rod in a chromosome is called a chromatid. The two chromatids are held together by a structure called a centromere. As the cell progresses through metaphase, anaphase, and telophase, the chromatids separate from each other and move to opposite ends of the cell. Then two nuclear envelopes form around the chromatids at the two ends of the cell.

After mitosis, the final stage of the cell cycle, called **cytokinesis**, completes the process of cell division. **During cytokinesis, the cytoplasm divides, distributing the organelles into each of the two new cells.** Each daughter cell has the same number of chromosomes as the original parent cell. At the end of cytokinesis, each cell enters interphase, and the cycle begins again. The length of each stage and cell cycle varies, depending on the type of cell.

DNA replication ensures that each daughter cell will have all of the genetic information it needs to carry out its activities. The two sides of the DNA ladder are made up of alternating sugar and phosphate molecules. Each rung of the DNA ladder is made up of a pair of molecules called nitrogen bases. There are four kinds of nitrogen bases: adenine, thymine, guanine, and cytosine. Adenine pairs only with thymine, and guanine pairs only with cytosine. DNA replication begins when the two sides of the DNA molecule unwind and separate. Next, nitrogen bases that are floating in the nucleus pair up with the bases on each half of the DNA molecule. **Because of the way in which the nitrogen bases pair with one another, the order of the bases in each new DNA molecule exactly matches the order in the original DNA molecule.** Once the new bases are attached, two new DNA molecules are formed.

Cell Processes and Energy ▪ *Reading/Notetaking Guide*

Cell Division (pp. 127–134)

This section explains how cells grow, divide, and specialize.

Use Target Reading Skills

As you read, make an outline to show the relationships between main ideas and supporting ideas. Use the headings, subheadings, Key Terms, and Key Concepts to help you complete the outline.

I. Stage 1: Interphase
    A.
    B.
    C.
    D.
    E.

II.
    A.
    B.
    C.
    D.
    E.
    F.
    G.
    H.

III.
    A.
    B.
    C.
    D.
    E.

IV.
    A.
    B.
    C.
    D.
    E.
    F.
    G.
    H.

Cell Processes and Energy • *Reading/Notetaking Guide*

Cell Division *(continued)*

Stage 1: Interphase *(p. 128)*

1. The regular sequence of growth and division that cells undergo is called the _____.

2. List three things that the cell is doing during interphase.

   a. _____

   b. _____

   c. _____

3. Circle the letter of the specific process during which the cell copies its DNA.

   a. interphase
   b. cytokinesis
   c. replication
   d. division

Stage 2: Mitosis *(pp. 129–131)*

4. Circle the letter of each sentence that is true about mitosis.

   a. The cell makes a copy of its DNA.
   b. The cell membrane pinches in around the middle of the cell.
   c. The cell's nucleus divides into two new nuclei.
   d. One copy of DNA is distributed into each daughter cell.

Match the phases of mitosis with the events that occur in each.

Event	Phase
____ 5. The centromeres split and the chromatids separate.	**a.** prophase
____ 6. The chromatin condenses to form chromosomes.	**b.** metaphase
____ 7. A new nuclear envelope forms around each region of chromosomes.	**c.** anaphase
____ 8. The chromosomes line up across the center of the cell.	**d.** telophase

Cell Processes and Energy ▪ *Reading/Notetaking Guide*

9. Label the parts of the structure in the diagram below.

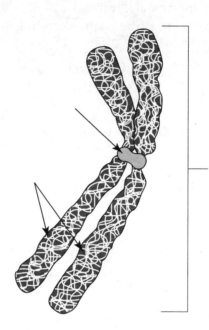

Stage 3: Cytokinesis (p. 132)

10. During cytokinesis the _____ divides, distributing the organelles into each of the two new cells.

11. Is the following sentence true or false? During cytokinesis in plant cells, the new cell membrane forms before the new cell wall does.

_____

Cell Processes and Energy ▪ *Reading/Notetaking Guide*

Cell Division *(continued)*

12. Complete this cycle diagram, which shows the events in the cell cycle, including the phases of mitosis. Write each event in a separate circle.

The Cell Cycle

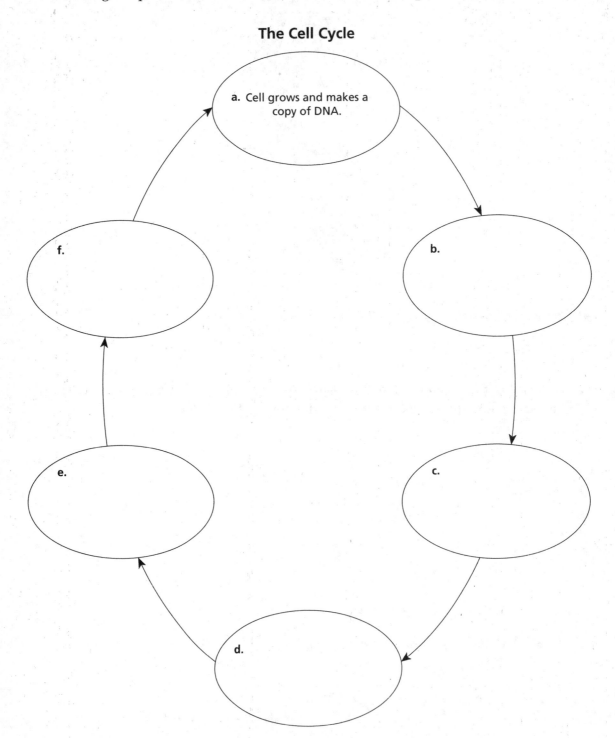

Cell Processes and Energy • *Reading/Notetaking Guide*

Structure and Replication of DNA (pp. 133–134)

13. Why does a cell make a copy of its DNA before mitosis occurs?

_____

_____

14. Circle the letter of each molecule that makes up the sides of the DNA ladder.

    a. deoxyribose

    b. glucose

    c. phosphate

    d. oxygen

15. Name the nitrogen bases that pair up to make up the rungs of the DNA ladder.

    a. _____ pairs with _____.

    b. _____ pairs with _____.

16. Complete the flowchart to show what happens during DNA replication.

DNA Replication

```
┌─────────────────────────────────────────────────────────┐
│  The two sides of the DNA molecule                        │
│  _____ and _____. │
└─────────────────────────────────────────────────────────┘
                          │
                          ▼
┌─────────────────────────────────────────────────────────┐
│  Nitrogen bases floating in the nucleus pair up with the  │
│  _____ on each half of the DNA molecule. │
└─────────────────────────────────────────────────────────┘
                          │
                          ▼
┌─────────────────────────────────────────────────────────┐
│  When the new bases are attached, two new                 │
│  _____ are formed.                   │
└─────────────────────────────────────────────────────────┘
```

Cell Differentiation

Key Concepts

- What is cell differentiation?
- What factors influence how and when cells differentiate within different organisms?

Cell division alone cannot explain the development of new structures. If cells only divided, the result would be a big ball of identical cells. Instead, cells differentiate. **Cell differentiation** is the process by which cells change in structure and become capable of carrying out specialized functions. **As cells differentiate, they become different from one another. They also form groups made of similarly specialized cells. These groups then form tissues and organs.**

Plants, animals, and other multicellular organisms begin their lives as one cell. Through mitosis and differentiation, the single cell becomes an organism with specialized structures. When cells differentiate, they also become organized. At first, they group into tissues. Tissues are groups of specialized cells that work together to carry out specific functions. Groups of tissues also combine to form organs. Systems are groups of organs that function together. As development continues, more fine-grained differentiation may take place.

During development, each cell becomes fixed—or set—in how it will differentiate. The plan that determines which type of cell it will become is coded in the DNA in the cell's nucleus. Differentiation occurs when certain sections of DNA are turned off. The active DNA then guides how the cell develops. **Once a cell's future has been determined, when and how much it changes depends on its DNA, its function, and the type of organism.**

Some animals, like reptiles and crustaceans, can grow a limb or tail to replace a lost one. Cells at the point of injury can differentiate, forming new muscle, bone, blood, and nerves. The replacement of lost body parts does not occur in humans. Once human cells differentiate, they usually lose the ability to become other types of cells. However, humans do produce cells— called **stem cells**—that can differentiate throughout life. Stem cells exist throughout the body, and they respond to certain needs in the body by becoming specialized cells. For example, your body needs a constant supply of red blood cells to replace older ones. Every day, stem cells produce new red blood cells.

Cells differentiate in developing plants in much the same way that they do in animals. Differentiated cells group together to form tissues that make up the roots, stems, and leaves. Adult plants have the ability to grow bigger throughout their lives. This growth happens because certain cells in the roots and stems of plants are not fixed in their development. These cells can undergo rapid cell division and differentiate, increasing the size of the roots and stems.

Cell Processes and Energy • *Reading/Notetaking Guide*

Cell Differentiation (pp. 136–139)

This section explains cell differentiation and the factors that influence how and when cells differentiate within different organisms.

Use Target Reading Skills

As you read, make an outline to show the relationships between main ideas and supporting ideas. Use the headings, subheadings, Key Terms, and Key Concepts to help you complete the outline.

I. What Is Cell Differentiation?
   A.
   B.
   C.
   D.
   E.

II.
   A.
   B.
   C.
   D.
   E.
   F.
   G.

What Is Cell Differentiation? (pp. 136–138)

1. What is cell differentiation?

   _____

   _____

2. Through _____ and _____, the single cell that an organism begins its life as becomes an organism with specialized structures.

3. Is the following sentence true or false? Cells become capable of carrying out specialized functions when they differentiate in structure.

   _____

4. List the three ways in which cells become organized when they differentiate.

   a. _____
   b. _____
   c. _____

Cell Processes and Energy • *Reading/Notetaking Guide*

How Cells Differentiate (pp. 138–139)

5. Circle the letter of each sentence that is true about how cells differentiate.

   a. The plan for what a cell will become is coded in its DNA.

   b. Differentiation occurs when certain sections of DNA are turned off.

   c. How much and when a cell changes depends on its function and its organelles.

   d. All cells differentiate completely during development.

6. Why can some lizards grow new tails?

   _____

   _____

7. What are stem cells?

   _____

   _____

   _____

8. Is the following sentence true or false? Plants can continue to grow all of their lives because certain cells in their roots and stems are not fixed in their development. _____

Mendel's Work

Key Concepts

- What were the results of Mendel's experiments, or crosses?
- What controls the inheritance of traits in organisms?

Heredity is the passing of physical characteristics from parents to offspring. Gregor Mendel was curious about the different forms of characteristics, or **traits,** of pea plants. Mendel's work was the foundation of **genetics,** the scientific study of heredity.

A new organism begins to form when egg and sperm join in the process called **fertilization.** Before fertilization can happen in pea plants, pollen must reach the pistil of a pea flower through pollination. Pea plants are usually self-pollinating, meaning pollen from a flower lands on the pistil of the same flower. Mendel developed a method by which he cross-pollinated, or "crossed," pea plants.

Mendel crossed two pea plants that differed in height. He crossed purebred tall plants with purebred short plants. These parent plants, the P generation, were **purebred** because they were the offspring of many generations that have the same trait. **In all of Mendel's crosses, only one form of the trait appeared in the F_1 generation. However, in the F_2 generation, the "lost" form of the trait always reappeared in about one fourth of the plants.** From his results, Mendel reasoned that individual factors, one from each parent, control the inheritance of traits. The factors that control each trait exist in pairs. One factor in a pair can hide the other factor. Today, scientists call the factors that control traits **genes.** The different forms of a gene are called **alleles.**

An organism's traits are controlled by the alleles it inherits from its parents. Some alleles are dominant, while other alleles are recessive. A **dominant allele** is one whose trait always shows up in the organism when the allele is present. A **recessive allele** is hidden whenever the dominant allele is present. A trait controlled by a recessive allele will only show up if the organism does not have the dominant allele.

In Mendel's cross, the purebred tall plant has two alleles for tall stems. The purebred short plant has two alleles for short stems. The F_1 plants are all **hybrids:** they have two different alleles for the trait—one allele for tall stems and one for short stems. Geneticists use a capital letter to represent a dominant allele and a lowercase version of the same letter for the recessive allele.

Mendel's discovery was not recognized during his lifetime. In 1900, three different scientists rediscovered Mendel's work. Because of his work, Mendel is often called the Father of Genetics.

Genetics: The Science of Heredity ▪ *Reading/Notetaking Guide*

Mendel's Work (pp. 154–159)

This section describes how Gregor Mendel identified the method by which characteristics are passed from parents to their offspring.

Use Target Reading Skills

As you read, complete the outline about Mendel's work. Use the red headings for the main idea and the blue headings for the supporting ideas.

> **I. Mendel's experiments**
>   A. Crossing pea plants
>   1.
>   2.
>   B.
>   C.
> **II.**
>   A.
>   B.
>   C.

Introduction (p. 154)

1. Gregor Mendel experimented with hundreds of pea plants to understand the process of _____.

Match the term with its definition.

	Term		Definition
____	**2.** heredity	**a.**	The scientific study of heredity
____	**3.** genetics	**b.**	Physical characteristics
____	**4.** traits	**c.**	The passing of traits from parents to offspring

Mendel's Experiments (pp. 155–156)

5. In a flower, the female sex cells, or eggs, are produced by the _____. Pollen, which contains the male sex cells, or sperm, is produced by the _____.

6. What are purebred organisms?

_____

_____

_____

Genetics: The Science of Heredity • *Reading/Notetaking Guide*

7. Complete the flowchart below to summarize Mendel's first experiment with pea plants.

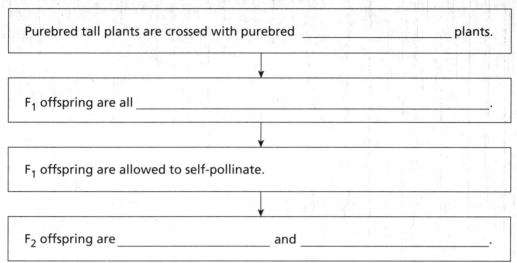

Mendel's Experiment

Purebred tall plants are crossed with purebred _____ plants.

↓

F_1 offspring are all _____.

↓

F_1 offspring are allowed to self-pollinate.

↓

F_2 offspring are _____ and _____.

8. Circle the letter of other traits in garden peas that Mendel studied.

   a. seed size, seed shape, seed color
   b. seed color, pod color, flower shape
   c. flower size, pod shape, seed coat color
   d. pod color, seed shape, flower position

9. Two forms of the trait of seed shape in pea plants are _____ and _____.

Dominant and Recessive Alleles (pp. 157–159)

10. Circle the letter of each sentence that is true about alleles.

   a. Recessive alleles are never present when dominant alleles are present.
   b. Alleles are different forms of a gene.
   c. A trait controlled by a dominant allele always shows up in the organism when the allele is present.
   d. Recessive alleles hide dominant alleles.

11. Is the following sentence true or false? Only pea plants that have two recessive alleles for short stems will be short. _____

Genetics: The Science of Heredity ▪ *Reading/Notetaking Guide*

Mendel's Work *(continued)*

Match the pea plant with its combination of alleles.

Pea Plant	Combination of Alleles
____ **12.** purebred short	**a.** Two alleles for tall stems
____ **13.** purebred tall	**b.** One allele for tall stems and one allele for short stems
____ **14.** hybrid tall	**c.** Two alleles for short stems

15. A dominant allele is represented by a(n) _____ letter.

16. A recessive allele is represented by a(n) _____ letter.

17. How might a geneticist write the alleles to show that a tall pea plant has one allele for tall stems and one allele for short stems?

_____

18. Is the following sentence true or false? Because of Mendel's work, he is often called the Father of Genetics. _____

Probability and Heredity

Key Concepts

- What is probability, and how does it help explain the results of genetic crosses?

- What is meant by genotype and phenotype?

- What is codominance?

Probability is a number that describes how likely it is that an event will occur. The principles of probability predict what is *likely* to occur, not necessarily what *will* occur. For example, in a coin toss, the coin will land either heads up or tails up. Each of these two events is equally likely to happen. In other words, there is a 1 in 2 chance that a tossed coin will land heads up, and a 1 in 2 chance that it will land tails up. A 1 in 2 chance can be expressed as the fraction $1/2$ or as a percent, 50 percent. The result of one coin toss does not affect the result of the next toss. Each event occurs independently.

When Mendel analyzed the results of his crosses in peas, he carefully counted all the offspring. Over time, he realized that he could apply the principles of probability to his crosses. Mendel was the first scientist to recognize that the principles of probability can be used to predict the results of genetic crosses.

A tool that applies the laws of probability to genetics is a Punnett square. A **Punnett square** is a chart that shows all the possible combinations of alleles that can result from a genetic cross. Geneticists use Punnett squares to show all the possible outcomes of a genetic cross and to determine the probability of a particular outcome. In a Punnett square, all the possible alleles from one parent are written across the top. All the possible alleles from the other parent are written down the left side. The combined alleles in the boxes of the Punnett square represent all the possible combinations in the offspring. **In a genetic cross, the allele that each parent will pass on to its offspring is based on probability.**

Two useful terms that geneticists use to describe organisms are **phenotype** and **genotype. An organism's phenotype is its physical appearance, or visible traits. An organism's genotype is its genetic makeup, or allele combinations.** When an organism has two identical alleles for a trait, the organism is said to be **homozygous** for that trait. An organism that has two different alleles for a trait is said to be **heterozygous** for that trait.

For all of the traits in peas that Mendel studied, one allele was dominant while the other was recessive. This is not always the case. In an inheritance pattern called **codominance, the alleles are neither dominant nor recessive. As a result, both alleles are expressed in the offspring.** Codominant alleles are written as capital letters with superscripts to show that neither is recessive.

Genetics: The Science of Heredity ▪ *Reading/Notetaking Guide*

Probability and Heredity (pp. 162–167)

This section explains what probability is and how the laws of probability can be used in the study of genetics.

Use Target Reading Skills

After you read the section, reread the paragraphs that contain definitions of Key Terms. Use all the information you have learned to write a definition of each Key Term in your own words.

probability _____

Punnett square _____

phenotype _____

genotype _____

homozygous _____

heterozygous _____

codominance _____

Principles of Probability (pp. 162–163)

1. A number that describes how likely it is that an event will occur is called

   _____.

2. Circle the letter of each answer that equals the probability that a tossed coin will land heads up.

   a. 1 in 2
   b. $1/2$
   c. 50 percent
   d. 20 percent

3. Is the following sentence true or false? When you toss a coin 20 times, you will always get 10 heads and 10 tails. _____

4. If you toss a coin five times and it lands heads up each time, can you expect the coin to land heads up on the sixth toss? Explain.

   _____

   _____

Genetics: The Science of Heredity ▪ *Reading/Notetaking Guide*

Probability and Genetics (pp. 164–165)

5. When Mendel crossed two hybrid plants for stem height (*Tt*), what results did he always get?

_____

_____

_____

6. Mendel realized that the principles of probability could be used to _____ the results of genetic crosses.

7. A chart that shows all the possible combinations of alleles that can result from a genetic cross is called a(n) _____.

8. In a genetic cross, the _____ that each parent passes to its offspring is based on _____.

9. Write in the alleles of the parents and the possible allele combinations of the offspring in the Punnett square below. Both parents are tall. Three of the offspring are tall, and one is short.

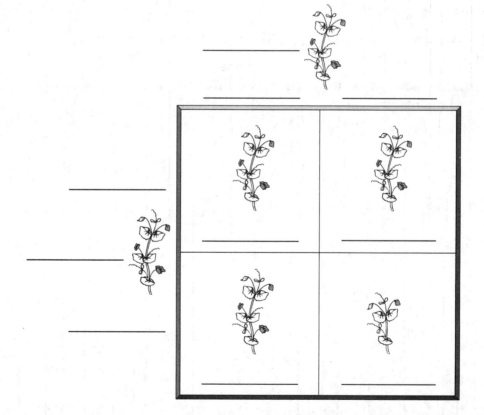

Genetics: The Science of Heredity ▪ *Reading/Notetaking Guide*

Probability and Heredity *(continued)*

Phenotypes and Genotypes (p. 166)

Match the term with its definition.

Term	Definition
_____ **10.** phenotype	**a.** Describes an organism with two identical alleles for a trait
_____ **11.** genotype	**b.** An organism's physical appearance, or visible traits
_____ **12.** homozygous	**c.** An organism's genetic makeup, or allele combinations
_____ **13.** heterozygous	**d.** Describes an organism that has two different alleles for a trait

14. Mendel used the term _____ to describe heterozygous pea plants.

Codominance (p. 167)

15. Is the following sentence true or false? In codominance, the alleles are neither dominant nor recessive. _____

16. In cattle, red hair and white hair are codominant. Cattle with both white hair and red hair are _____.

Chapter 5 Genetics: The Science of Heredity ▪ *Section 3 Summary*

The Cell and Inheritance

Key Concepts

■ What role do chromosomes play in inheritance?

■ What events occur during meiosis?

■ What is the relationship between chromosomes and genes?

In the early 1900s, scientists were working to identify the cell structures that carried Mendel's hereditary factors, or genes. In 1903, Walter Sutton observed that sex cells in grasshoppers had half the number of chromosomes as the body cells. He also noticed that each grasshopper offspring had exactly the same number of chromosomes in its body cells as each of the parents. He reasoned that the chromosomes in body cells actually occurred in pairs, with one chromosome in each pair coming from the male and the other coming from the female.

From his observations, Sutton concluded that paired alleles were carried on paired chromosomes. He proposed the chromosome theory of inheritance. **According to the chromosome theory of inheritance, genes are carried from parents to their offspring on chromosomes.**

Organisms produce sex cells during meiosis. **Meiosis** is the process by which the number of chromosomes is reduced by half to form sex cells—sperm and eggs. **During meiosis, the chromosome pairs separate and are distributed to two different cells. The resulting sex cells have only half as many chromosomes as the other cells in the organism.** When they combine, each sex cell contributes half the number of chromosomes to produce offspring with the correct number of chromosomes.

A Punnett square is a way to show the events that occur during meiosis. When chromosome pairs separate, so do the alleles carried on the chromosomes. One allele from each pair goes to each sex cell.

Chromosomes are made up of many genes joined together like beads on a string. Each chromosome contains a large number of genes, each gene controlling a particular trait. Each chromosome pair has the same genes. The genes are lined up in the same order on both chromosomes. However, the alleles for some of the genes might differ from each other, making the organism heterozygous for some traits. If the alleles are the same, the organism is homozygous for those traits.

Genetics: The Science of Heredity ▪ *Reading/Notetaking Guide*

The Cell and Inheritance (pp. 170–174)

This section describes the process of meiosis and how one set of chromosomes from each parent is passed on to the offspring.

Use Target Reading Skills

As you read, take notes on the evidence that supports the hypothesis that genes are found on chromosomes. Write the evidence in the graphic organizer below.

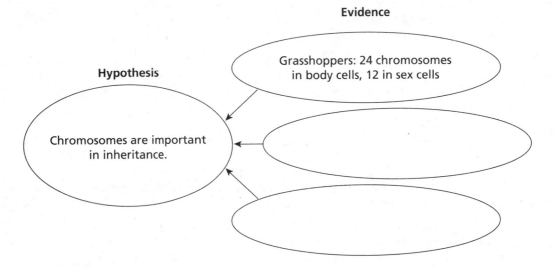

Evidence

Hypothesis

Chromosomes are important in inheritance.

Grasshoppers: 24 chromosomes in body cells, 12 in sex cells

Introduction

1. What happens during sexual reproduction?

   _____

Chromosomes and Inheritance (p. 171)

2. Circle the letter of each sentence that is true about what Walter Sutton observed about chromosome number.

   a. Grasshopper sex cells have half the number of chromosomes as body cells.
   b. Grasshopper body cells have half the number of chromosomes as sex cells.
   c. Grasshopper body cells and sex cells have the same number of chromosomes.
   d. A diploid cell contains two sets of chromosomes, one set from each parent.

3. What is the chromosome theory of inheritance?

   _____

   _____

Meiosis (pp. 172–173)

4. What is meiosis?

   _____

   _____

Genetics: The Science of Heredity • *Reading/Notetaking Guide*

5. Complete the cycle diagram to describe the events that occur during meiosis and fertilization.

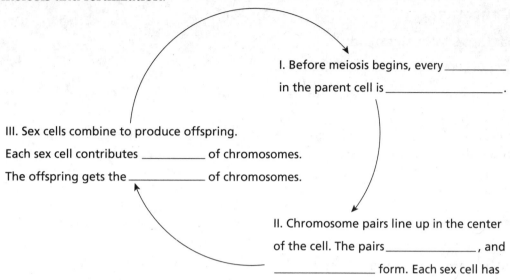

I. Before meiosis begins, every _____ in the parent cell is _____.

III. Sex cells combine to produce offspring. Each sex cell contributes _____ of chromosomes. The offspring gets the _____ of chromosomes.

II. Chromosome pairs line up in the center of the cell. The pairs _____, and _____ form. Each sex cell has _____ chromosomes.

6. A Punnett square is a way to show the events that occur during _____.

7. Is the following sentence true or false? During meiosis, the two alleles for each gene stay together. _____

8. If the male parent cell is heterozygous for a trait, *Tt*, what alleles could the sperm cells possibly have?

   _____

   _____

A Lineup of Genes (p. 174)

9. How many pairs of chromosomes do human body cells contain?

   _____

10. What are chromosomes made up of?

   _____

   _____

11. How are the genes lined up in a pair of chromosomes?

   _____

   _____

   _____

Chapter 5 Genetics: The Science of Heredity • *Section 4 Summary*

Genes, DNA, and Proteins

Key Concepts

■ What forms the genetic code?

■ How does a cell produce proteins?

■ How can mutations affect an organism?

Genes control the production of proteins in the cells of an organism. Proteins determine the size, shape, and other traits of organisms. Recall that chromosomes are composed mostly of DNA. A DNA molecule is made up of four nitrogen bases—adenine (A), thymine (T), guanine (G), and cytosine (C). **The order of the nitrogen bases along a gene forms a genetic code that specifies what type of protein will be produced.** In the genetic code, a group of three DNA bases codes for one specific amino acid.

During protein synthesis, the cell uses information from a gene on a chromosome to produce a specific protein. Protein synthesis occurs on the ribosomes in the cytoplasm of the cell. DNA, however, is located in the nucleus. Before protein synthesis occurs, a genetic "messenger" called ribonucleic acid, or RNA, is made based on a code in the DNA. Unlike DNA, RNA has only one strand and has uracil instead of thymine.

There are several types of RNA involved in protein synthesis. **Messenger RNA** copies the coded message from the DNA in the nucleus, and carries it to the ribosomes in the cytoplasm. **Transfer RNA** carries amino acids and adds them to the growing protein.

In the first step of protein synthesis, the DNA molecule "unzips" and directs the production of messenger RNA. The messenger RNA enters the cytoplasm and attaches to a ribosome, where it provides the code for the protein molecule that will form. Molecules of transfer RNA attach to the messenger RNA and "read" the message by pairing up three-letter codes to bases on the messenger RNA. The protein molecule grows longer as each transfer RNA molecule puts the amino acid it is carrying along the chain.

Sometimes changes called **mutations** occur in a gene or chromosome. **Mutations can cause a cell to produce an incorrect protein during protein synthesis. As a result, the organism's trait, or phenotype, may be different from what it normally would have been.** If a mutation occurs in a body cell, the mutation affects only the cell that carries it. However, if a mutation occurs in a sex cell, the mutation can be passed on to an offspring and affect the offspring's phenotype. Some mutations are the result of small changes in an organism's hereditary material. Others occur when chromosomes don't separate correctly during meiosis.

Some mutations are harmful to an organism. A few mutations, however, are helpful, and still others are neither harmful nor helpful. A mutation is harmful if it reduces an organism's chance for survival and reproduction. Whether or not a mutation is harmful depends partly on the organism's environment.

Genetics: The Science of Heredity · *Reading/Notetaking Guide*

Genes, DNA, and Proteins (pp. 175–181)

This section tells what forms the genetic code, how cells produce proteins, and how mutations can affect organisms.

Use Target Reading Skills

As you read, take notes and complete the flowchart below to show protein synthesis. Put the steps of the process in separate boxes in the flowchart in the order in which they occur.

Protein Synthesis

DNA provides code to form messenger RNA.

↓

Messenger RNA attaches to ribosome.

↓

↓

The Genetic Code (p. 176)

1. Circle the letter of each sentence that is true about genes, chromosomes, and proteins.

    a. Genes control the production of proteins in an organism's cells.
    b. Proteins help determine the size, shape, and other traits of an organism.
    c. Chromosomes are made up mostly of proteins.
    d. A single gene on a chromosome contains only one pair of nitrogen bases.

2. What are the four nitrogen bases that make up a DNA molecule?

    _____

    _____

Genetics: The Science of Heredity · *Reading/Notetaking Guide*

Genes, DNA, and Proteins (*continued*)

3. What is the genetic code?

   _____

   _____

   _____

4. One group of three nitrogen bases codes for one _____.

How Cells Make Proteins (pp. 177–179)

5. During protein synthesis, the cell uses information from a
   _____ on a chromosome to produce a specific
   _____.

6. Proteins are made on _____ in the cytoplasm of the cell.

7. Complete the Venn diagram to show some of the similarities and
   differences between DNA and RNA. Tell where each nucleic acid is
   located and what bases it contains.

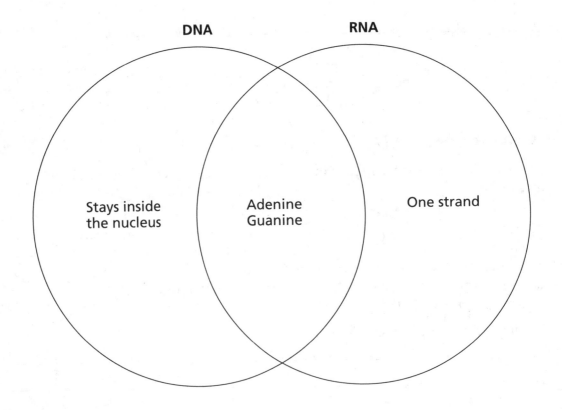

DNA

RNA

Stays inside
the nucleus

Adenine
Guanine

One strand

Genetics: The Science of Heredity · *Reading/Notetaking Guide*

8. List the two kinds of RNA, and describe their jobs.

   a. _____

   _____

   _____

   b. _____

   _____

   _____

9. Circle the letter of the first step in protein synthesis.

   a. Transfer RNA carries amino acids to the ribosome.
   b. The ribosome releases the completed protein chain.
   c. Messenger RNA enters the cytoplasm and attaches to a ribosome.
   d. DNA "unzips" to direct the production of a strand of messenger RNA.

10. Circle the letter of the last step in protein synthesis.

    a. Transfer RNA attaches to the messenger RNA and reads the message by matching up with three-letter codes of bases.
    b. The protein chain grows longer as each transfer RNA molecule adds an amino acid.
    c. Messenger RNA enters the cytoplasm and attaches to a ribosome.
    d. DNA "unzips" to direct the production of a strand of messenger RNA.

Mutations (pp. 180–181)

11. What is a mutation?

    _____

    _____

    _____

12. How can mutations affect protein synthesis in cells? What is the result?

    _____

    _____

    _____

    _____

Genetics: The Science of Heredity · *Reading/Notetaking Guide*

Genes, DNA, and Proteins *(continued)*

13. Circle the letter of each sentence that is true about mutations.

   a. Cells with mutations will always make normal proteins.

   b. Some mutations occur when one nitrogen base is substituted for another.

   c. Some mutations occur when chromosomes don't separate correctly during meiosis.

   d. Mutations that occur in a body cell can be passed on to an offspring.

14. Mutations can be a source of genetic _____.

15. Is the following sentence true or false? All mutations are harmful.
   _____

16. Mutations that are _____ improve an organism's chances for survival and reproduction.

17. Whether a mutation is harmful or helpful depends partly on an organism's _____.

Chapter 6 Modern Genetics · *Section 1 Summary*

Human Inheritance

Key Concepts

■ What are some patterns of inheritance in humans?

■ What are the functions of the sex chromosomes?

■ What is the relationship between genes and the environment?

Many human traits are controlled by a single gene with one dominant allele and one recessive allele. As with tall and short pea plants, these human traits have two distinctly different phenotypes, or physical appearances. For example, the allele for a widow's peak, which is a hairline that comes to a point in the middle of the forehead, is dominant over the allele for a straight hairline.

Some human traits are controlled by single genes with two alleles, and others by single genes with multiple alleles. Still other traits are controlled by many genes that act together. Height and skin color are both examples of human traits controlled by many genes. When more than one gene controls a trait, there are many possible combinations of genes and alleles. For example, there is an enormous variety of phenotypes for height, and human skin color ranges from almost white to nearly black, with many shades in between.

Some human traits are controlled by a single gene that has more than two alleles. Such a gene is said to have **multiple alleles**—three or more forms of a gene that code for a single trait. An example of a human trait that is controlled by a gene with multiple alleles is blood type. There are four main blood types—A, B, AB, and O—controlled by three alleles.

The **sex chromosomes** are one of 23 pairs of chromosomes in each body cell. **The sex chromosomes carry genes that determine whether a person is male or female. They also carry genes that determine other traits.** If you are female, you have two X chromosomes. If you are male, you have an X and a Y chromosome. Whether you inherited an X or Y chromosome from your father determines your sex.

Genes on the X and Y chromosomes are often called **sex-linked genes.** Traits controlled by sex-linked genes are called sex-linked traits. Because males have only one X chromosome, males are more likely than females to have a sex-linked trait that is controlled by a recessive allele. One example of a sex-linked trait that is controlled by a recessive allele is red-green colorblindness. A **carrier** is a person who has one recessive allele for a sex-linked trait and one dominant allele. Although a carrier does not have the trait, the carrier can pass the recessive allele on to his or her offspring. In the case of sex-linked traits, only females can be carriers.

The effects of genes are often altered by the environment. **Many of an organism's characteristics are determined by an interaction between genes and the environment.** Several genes determine human height. However, environment also influences people's heights. A diet lacking in proteins, certain minerals, and certain vitamins can prevent a person from growing as tall as might be possible.

Modern Genetics · *Reading/Notetaking Guide*

Human Inheritance (pp. 192–197)

This section explains some patterns of inheritance in humans. It also describes the functions of the sex chromosomes and the relationship between genes and the environment.

Use Target Reading Skills

As you read, write the main idea—the biggest or most important idea—in the graphic organizer below. Then write three supporting details that further explain the main idea.

Main Idea

Human traits are controlled by single genes with two alleles, single genes with . . .

Detail	**Detail**	**Detail**
a.	b.	c.

Patterns of Human Inheritance (pp. 192–193)

1. The probability that two heterozygous parents for widow's peak will have a child with a straight hairline is _____ percent.

2. In what three ways are human traits controlled?

_____

_____

_____

Modern Genetics · *Reading/Notetaking Guide*

3. A gene with three or more alleles for a single trait has _____.

4. Is the following sentence true or false? Even though a gene has multiple alleles, a person can carry only two of those alleles. _____

5. Complete the table by writing all possible combinations of alleles for each blood type.

Blood Types	
Blood Type	**Combination of Alleles**
A	
B	
AB	
O	

6. Why do some human traits, such as height and hair color, show a large number of phenotypes?

   _____

   _____

   _____

7. Is the following sentence true or false? Skin color is controlled by more than one gene. _____

Modern Genetics · *Reading/Notetaking Guide*

Human Inheritance (continued)

The Sex Chromosomes (pp. 194–196)

8. Is the following sentence true or false? Genes on chromosomes determine whether a baby is a boy or a girl. _____

9. Females have two _____ chromosomes. Males have one _____ chromosome and one _____ chromosome.

10. Circle the letter of each sentence that is true about human sex chromosomes.

   a. All eggs carry one X chromosome.
   b. Half of a male's sperm cells have an X chromosome.
   c. None of a male's sperm cells have a Y chromosome.
   d. The egg determines the sex of the child.

11. Genes on the X and Y chromosomes are called _____.

12. Why are males more likely than females to have a sex-linked trait that is controlled by a recessive allele?

   _____

   _____

13. Is the following question true or false? A carrier for colorblindness is colorblind. _____

14. Why is a son who receives the allele for colorblindness from his mother always colorblind?

   _____

   _____

   _____

The Effect of Environment (p. 197)

15. The effects of genes are often altered by the _____.

16. List one environmental factor that can affect a person's height.

   _____

Chapter 6 Modern Genetics • *Section 2 Summary*

Human Genetic Disorders

Key Concepts

- What are two major causes of genetic disorders in humans?
- How do geneticists trace the inheritance of traits?
- How are genetic disorders diagnosed and treated?

A **genetic disorder** is an abnormal condition that a person inherits through genes or chromosomes. **Some genetic disorders are caused by mutations in the DNA of genes. Other disorders are caused by changes in the overall structure or number of chromosomes.**

Cystic fibrosis is a genetic disorder in which the body produces abnormally thick mucus in the lungs and intestines, making it hard to breathe and digest food. The allele that causes cystic fibrosis is recessive. Currently there is no cure for cystic fibrosis, although there are treatments to help control the symptoms.

Sickle-cell disease is a genetic disorder that affects hemoglobin, the protein in blood that carries oxygen. People with sickle-cell disease suffer from lack of oxygen in the blood and experience pain and weakness. The allele that causes sickle-cell disease is codominant with the normal allele. People with two sickle-cell alleles have the disease. People with one sickle-cell allele produce both normal and abnormal hemoglobin but usually do not have symptoms of the disease. Currently there is no cure for sickle-cell disease. However, treatments can lessen the pain and other symptoms.

Hemophilia is a genetic disorder in which the blood clots very slowly or not at all. People with the disorder do not produce one of the proteins needed for normal blood clotting. Hemophilia is caused by a recessive allele on the X chromosome.

Down syndrome is a genetic disorder that is due to an extra copy of chromosome 21. Most often Down syndrome occurs when the chromosomes fail to separate properly during meiosis. People with Down syndrome have a distinctive physical appearance and some degree of mental retardation. Many people with Down syndrome lead full, active lives.

Geneticists trace the inheritance of traits through several generations of a family. **One important tool that geneticists use to trace the inheritance of traits in humans is a pedigree.** A **pedigree** is a chart or "family tree" that tracks which members have a particular trait.

Today, doctors use tools such as karyotypes to help diagnose genetic disorders. People with genetic disorders are helped through medical care, education, job training, and other methods. To detect chromosomal disorders such as Down syndrome, a doctor examines the chromosomes from a person's cells. The doctor uses a **karyotype,** or picture of all the chromosomes in a cell, to examine the chromosomes. The chromosomes are arranged in pairs. A karyotype can reveal whether a person has the correct number of chromosomes in his or her cells.

A couple that has a family history or concern about a genetic disorder may turn to a genetic counselor for advice. Genetic counselors help couples understand their chances of having a child with a particular genetic disorder. Genetic counselors use tools such as karyotypes, pedigree charts, and Punnett squares.

Modern Genetics · *Reading/Notetaking Guide*

Human Genetic Disorders (pp. 198–202)

This section describes how changes in the DNA of some genes have affected certain traits in humans.

Use Target Reading Skills

As you read, compare and contrast the types of genetic disorders by completing the table below.

Disorder	Description	Cause
Cystic fibrosis	Abnormally thick mucus	Loss of three DNA bases
Sickle-cell disease		
Hemophilia		
Down syndrome		

Introduction (p. 198)

1. An abnormal condition that a person inherits through genes or chromosomes is called a(n) _____.

Causes of Genetic Disorders (p. 199)

2. What causes genetic disorders?

_____

_____

Modern Genetics ▪ *Reading/Notetaking Guide*

3. What is cystic fibrosis?

_____

_____

_____

4. Is the following sentence true or false? Cystic fibrosis is caused by a mutation that is the dominant allele of a gene. _____

5. Circle the letter of the protein that is not normal in people with sickle-cell disease.

    a. mucus   **b.** hemoglobin

    c. red blood cells   **d.** clotting protein

6. The allele for the sickle-cell trait is _____ with the normal allele.

7. Is the following sentence true or false? Hemophilia is caused by a dominant allele on the X chromosome. _____

8. Hemophilia occurs more often in _____.

9. Circle the letter of the cause of Down syndrome.

    a. recessive allele

    b. dominant allele

    c. too many chromosomes

    d. too few chromosomes

10. Down syndrome most often occurs when _____ fail to separate properly during meiosis.

Pedigrees (p. 200)

11. A chart or "family tree" that tracks which members of a family have a certain trait is called a(n) _____.

12. Is the following sentence true or false? On a pedigree, a circle represents a male. _____

Managing Genetic Disorders (pp. 201–202)

13. How can people be helped when they have a genetic disorder?

_____

_____

14. A _____ is a picture of all the chromosomes in a cell.

15. What is a karyotype used for? What can it reveal?

_____

_____

Chapter 6 Modern Genetics • *Section 3 Summary*

Advances in Genetics

Key Concepts

■ What are three ways of producing organisms with desired traits?

■ What are two applications of DNA technology in human genetics?

For thousands of years, people have tried to produce plants and animals with desirable traits. **Selective breeding, cloning, and genetic engineering are three methods for developing organisms with desirable traits.**

The process of selecting organisms with desired traits to be parents of the next generation is called **selective breeding.** People have used selective breeding with many different plants and animals. One selective breeding technique is called inbreeding. **Inbreeding** involves crossing two individuals that have similar characteristics. One goal of inbreeding is to produce breeds of organisms with specific traits. For example, by crossing turkeys that are plump and grow quickly, breeders can expect their offspring to have those desirable traits. Unfortunately, inbreeding also increases the probability that organisms may inherit alleles that lead to genetic disorders. Another selective breeding technique is called hybridization. In **hybridization,** breeders cross two genetically different individuals. The hybrid organism that results is bred to have the best traits from both parents. For example, a farmer might cross corn that produces many kernels with corn that is resistant to disease.

For some organisms, another technique, called cloning, can be used to produce offspring with desired traits. A **clone** is an organism that is genetically identical to the organism from which it was produced. One way to produce a clone of a plant is to cut and grow a small part of a plant, such as a leaf or stem. Several types of animals have been cloned in recent years.

Another technique for producing organisms with desired traits is called genetic engineering. In **genetic engineering,** genes from one organism are transferred into the DNA of another organism. Genetic engineering can produce medicines and improve food crops, and may some day correct human genetic disorders. In a type of genetic engineering called **gene therapy,** working copies of a gene may be inserted directly into the cells of a person with a genetic disorder. Some people are concerned about the long-term effects of genetic engineering.

Applications of DNA technology include studying the human genome in detail and identifying people. A **genome** is all the DNA in one cell of an organism. The main goal of the Human Genome Project has been to identify the DNA sequence of every gene in the human genome. From the Human Genome Project, scientists hope to learn more about what makes the body work and what causes things to go wrong. A genetic technique called DNA fingerprinting is used to identify people. No two people, except for identical twins, have the same DNA.

Modern Genetics • *Reading/Notetaking Guide*

Advances in Genetics (pp. 204–209)

This section describes some of the research in genetic technology and how it can be used.

Use Target Reading Skills

As you read, write the main idea in the graphic organizer below. Then write three supporting details that further explain the main idea.

Main Idea

Detail	Detail	Detail
a.	b.	c.

Selective Breeding (p. 205)

1. The process of selecting a few organisms with the desired traits to serve as parents of the next generation is called _____.

2. What is inbreeding? _____

   _____

3. Is the following sentence true or false? In hybridization, breeders cross two individuals that are genetically identical. _____

4. When breeders cross two genetically different individuals to produce an organism with the best traits from both parents, this breeding method is called _____.

Modern Genetics · *Reading/Notetaking Guide*

Advances in Genetics (continued)

Cloning (p. 206)

5. Circle the letter of each sentence that is true about cloning.

   a. A clone has exactly the same genes as the organism from which it was produced.

   b. A cutting is one way to make a clone of an animal.

   c. It's easier to clone an animal than it is to clone a plant.

6. Is the following sentence true or false? Cloning can be done only in animals. _____

Genetic Engineering (pp. 207–208)

7. In genetic engineering, genes from one organism are transferred into the _____ of another organism.

8. Complete this flowchart about genetic engineering in bacteria.

Genetic Engineering in Bacteria

Human DNA is spliced into the _____ , which is a small ring of DNA in bacteria.

↓

The _____ takes up the plasmid. It now contains the human gene.

↓

The bacterial cell reproduces the _____ that the human gene codes for.

9. What is gene therapy?

_____

_____

Learning About Human Genetics (p. 209)

10. All the DNA in one cell of an organism is a(n) _____.

11. What has been the goal of the Human Genome Project?

_____

_____

12. How is a DNA fingerprint produced?

_____

_____

Darwin's Theory

Key Concepts

- What important observations did Darwin make on his voyage?

- How did Darwin account for the diversity of species and the differences between similar species?

- How does natural selection lead to evolution?

In 1831, Charles Darwin left England on board the HMS *Beagle.* While on his voyage, he observed plants and animals he had never seen before. **Darwin's important observations included the diversity of living things, the remains of ancient organisms, and the characteristics of organisms on the Galápagos Islands.** Darwin saw many different species. A **species** is a group of similar organisms that can mate with each other and produce fertile offspring. Darwin saw the fossil bones of animals that had died long ago. A **fossil** is the preserved remains or traces of an organism that lived in the past.

In 1835, the *Beagle* reached the Galápagos Islands in the Pacific Ocean. Darwin was surprised that many of the plants and animals on the Galápagos Islands were similar to organisms on mainland South America. However, there were also important differences. Darwin inferred that a small number of different species had come to the islands from the mainland. Eventually, their offspring became different from the mainland relatives. The finches on the Galápagos Islands were noticeably different from one island to another. The most obvious differences were the varied sizes and shapes of the birds' beaks. Beak shape is an example of an **adaptation,** a trait that helps an organism survive and reproduce. **Darwin reasoned that plants or animals that arrived on the Galápagos Islands faced environmental factors that were different from those on the mainland. Perhaps, Darwin hypothesized, the species gradually changed over many generations and became better adapted to the new environments.** The gradual change in a species over time is called **evolution.** Darwin's ideas are often referred to as the theory of evolution. A **scientific theory** is a well-tested concept that explains a wide range of observations.

In his book *The Origin of Species,* Darwin proposed that evolution occurs by means of natural selection. **Natural selection** is the process by which individuals that are better adapted to their environment are more likely to survive and reproduce than other members of the same species. A number of factors affect the process of natural selection: overproduction, competition, and variations. Any difference between individuals of the same species is called a **variation.** Some variations make certain individuals better adapted to their environment because of helpful traits they possess. **Darwin proposed that, over a long time, natural selection can lead to change. Helpful variations may gradually accumulate in a species, while unfavorable ones may disappear.** Without variations, all members of a species would have the same traits, and natural selection would not occur. Only traits that are inherited, or controlled by genes, can be acted upon by natural selection.

Name _____ Date _____ Class _____

Darwin's Theory (pp. 200–207)

This section discusses Charles Darwin and his theories of evolution, which are based on what he saw during his trip around the world.

Use Target Reading Skills

In the graphic organizer, identify Darwin's important observations.

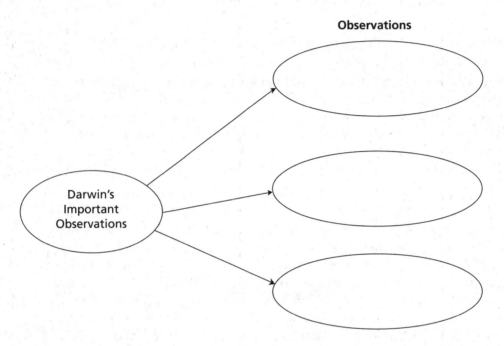

Darwin's Observations (p. 201)

1. Is the following sentence true or false? Charles Darwin was not surprised by the variety of living things he saw on his voyage around the world. _____

2. A group of similar organisms that can mate with each other and produce fertile offspring is called a(n) _____.

3. A(n) _____ is the preserved remains or traces of an organism that lived in the past.

Changes Over Time • *Reading/Notetaking Guide*

Galápagos Organisms (pp. 202–203)

4. Circle the letter of each sentence that is true about Darwin's observations.

   a. Many Galápagos organisms were similar to organisms on mainland South America.

   b. Iguanas on the Galápagos Islands had small claws for climbing trees.

   c. Darwin thought the ancestors of Galápagos animals and plants came from mainland South America.

   d. All tortoises living in the Galápagos Islands looked exactly the same.

5. Darwin noticed many differences among similar _____ as he traveled from one Galápagos island to the next.

Look at the bird beaks below. Match the bird beaks with the kind of food the bird eats.

Kind of Food   **Bird Beaks**

_____   **6.** insects

_____   **7.** seeds   **a.**   **b.**

8. A trait that helps an organism survive and reproduce is a(n) _____.

Evolution (p. 204)

9. Circle the letter of each sentence that is true about Darwin's conclusions.

   a. Darwin understood immediately why Galápagos organisms had many different adaptations.

   b. Darwin thought that Galápagos organisms gradually changed over many generations.

   c. Darwin believed that evolution had occurred on the Galápagos Islands.

   d. Selective breeding helped Darwin understand how evolution might occur.

10. What is evolution?

_____

Changes Over Time • *Reading/Notetaking Guide*

Darwin's Theory *(continued)*

11. Circle the letter of the term that means a well-tested concept that explains many observations.

    a. idea

    b. evolution

    c. scientific theory

    d. hypothesis

Natural Selection (pp. 205–207)

12. In his book *The Origin of Species,* Darwin explained that evolution occurs by means of _____.

13. Is the following sentence true or false? Individuals with variations that make them better adapted to their environment will not survive.

    _____

Match the factors that affect the process of natural selection with their definitions.

	Definitions	**Factors**
_____	14. Effect caused by limited food and other resources	**a.** overproduction
_____	15. Differences between individuals of the same species	**b.** competition
_____	16. Effect caused by species producing more offspring than can survive	**c.** variations

17. Is the following sentence true or false? Only traits that are controlled by genes can be acted upon by natural selection.

    _____

18. Is the following sentence true or false? Darwin knew all about genes and mutations. _____

19. Why would natural selection not occur without variations in species?

    _____

    _____

Evidence of Evolution

Key Concepts

- What evidence supports the theory of evolution?

- How do fossils form?

- What do scientists learn from fossils?

Modern-day organisms can provide clues about evolution. **Similar body structures, patterns of early development, molecular structure, and fossils all provide evidence that organisms have changed over time.** By comparing organisms, scientists can infer how closely related the organisms are in an evolutionary sense. Scientists compare body structures, development before birth, and DNA sequences to determine the evolutionary relationships among organisms.

The comparison of the structures of different organisms is called **comparative anatomy.** Fishes, amphibians, reptiles, birds, and mammals all have an internal skeleton with a backbone. This is why scientists classify all five groups of animals together as vertebrates. Presumably, these groups all inherited these similarities in structure from an early vertebrate ancestor that they shared. Similar structures that related species have inherited from a common ancestor are called homologous structures.

Scientists make inferences about evolutionary relationships by comparing how different species develop before birth. During early development, vertebrates have a tail and rows of tiny slits in their throats, suggesting that vertebrate species share a common ancestor. Two species with similar DNA and proteins probably evolved from a common ancestor.

Most fossils form when organisms that die become buried in sediments. The most common fossils are molds and casts. A **mold** is a hollow area in sediment in the shape of an organism. A **cast** is a solid copy of the shape of an organism. It is the opposite of a mold. A fossil may form when the remains of an organism become petrified. **Petrified fossils** are fossils in which minerals replace all or part of an organism. **Trace fossils** provide evidence of the activity of ancient organisms.

A **paleontologist** is a scientist who studies fossils. **The fossil record provides evidence about the history of life and past environments on Earth. In addition, scientists use fossils to study the speed at which evolution has occurred.** The fossil record shows that life on Earth has evolved, or changed over time. Simple, one-celled organisms have given rise to complex plants and animals. Fossils can show how an environment has changed or how Earth's surface has changed.

Scientists are not sure how rapidly species change. The theory of **gradualism** proposes that evolution occurs slowly but steadily. It states that tiny changes in a species gradually add up to major changes over very long periods of time. The theory of **punctuated equilibria** accounts for gaps in the fossil record. It states that species evolve quickly during relatively short periods.

Changes Over Time ▪ *Reading/Notetaking Guide*

Evidence of Evolution (pp. 210–216)

This section explains what evidence supports the theory of evolution, how fossils form, and what scientists learn from fossils.

Use Target Reading Skills

As you read, identify the evidence that supports the theory of evolution. Write the evidence in the graphic organizer.

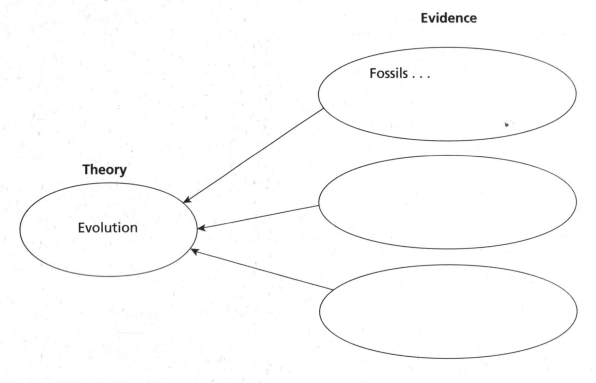

Evidence

Fossils . . .

Theory

Evolution

Changes Over Time · *Reading/Notetaking Guide*

Forms of Evidence (pp. 210–211)

1. Similar body structures that related species have inherited from a common ancestor are called _____.

2. What similarities in development lead scientists to infer that vertebrate species share a common ancestor?

    _____

    _____

    _____

3. Why do scientists classify fish, amphibians, reptiles, birds, and mammals together in one group?

    _____

    _____

    _____

4. How can DNA provide evidence of evolution?

    _____

    _____

How Do Fossils Form? (pp. 212–213)

5. Is the following sentence true or false? Most fossils form when living things die and are buried by sediments. _____

6. Is the following sentence true or false? The formation of fossils is a common event. _____

7. Explain how a fossil forms.

    _____

    _____

    _____

Changes Over Time • *Reading/Notetaking Guide*

Evidence of Evolution *(continued)*

8. Circle the letter of each sentence that is true about molds and casts.
    a. Both molds and casts copy the shape of ancient organisms.
    b. A mold forms when the hard part of an organism is buried in sediment.
    c. A cast is a hollow area in sediment in the shape of an organism.
    d. Molds and casts do not show details of the organism's structure.

9. Fossils in which minerals replace all or part of an organism are called _____ fossils.

10. Circle the letter of each trace fossil.
    a. footprints
    b. animal trails
    c. animal shells
    d. burrows

11. What can a scientist infer by looking at fossil footprints?

    _____

    _____

    _____

12. What are three ways that the remains of organisms have been preserved?
    a. _____

    b. _____

    c. _____

Learning From Fossils (pp. 214–216)

13. Scientists who study fossils are called _____.

14. All the information that paleontologists have gathered about past life is called the _____.

15. Circle the letter of each sentence that is true about the fossil record.
    a. It provides evidence for the history of life on Earth.
    b. It shows that organisms have changed over time.
    c. It reveals that complex organisms have given rise to simpler organisms.
    d. It provides evidence to support the theory of evolution.

Changes Over Time ▪ *Reading/Notetaking Guide*

16. Is the following sentence true or false? It is very difficult for scientists to learn about Earth's past environments by studying fossils.

_____

17. What is gradualism?

_____

_____

18. The theory of _____ accounts for the gaps in the fossil record.

19. What do most scientists believe about the rate of evolution?

_____

Chapter 7 Changes Over Time · *Section 3 Summary*

Evolution of Species

Key Concepts

- What factors have contributed to the diversity of species?

- How do new species form?

- How do scientists infer evolutionary relationships among species?

- What causes the extinction of species?

Different environments and genetic variation have over time, through natural selection, produced the variety of organisms that exist today. Over millions of years, natural selection has produced different species, each with adaptations enabling it to live in a specific habitat. An organism's **habitat** is the specific environment that produces the things the organism needs to live, grow, and reproduce.

Organisms within the same species do not all have identical traits. Some genetic differences, or variations, may result from mutations in DNA. Others may be caused by "reshuffling" of genes during meiosis. All the genetic variations in a species make up the total gene "pool" of that species. Many species have a lot of variety in their gene pools. These species can often adapt to changes in the environment because some individuals will have traits that let them survive in the new conditions. In some species, however, most of the organisms are similar genetically. Those species may have difficulty surviving environmental change.

A new species can form when a group of individuals remains isolated from the rest of its species long enough to evolve different traits. Isolation, or complete separation, happens when some members of a species become cut off from the rest of the species. Once a group becomes isolated, members of the isolated group can no longer mate with the rest of the species.

Some species are closely related to one another. **Scientists have combined the evidence from DNA, protein structure, fossils, early development, and body structure to determine the evolutionary relationships among species.** Scientists infer that species that have similar body structures and development patterns inherited many genes from a common ancestor. By comparing the sequence of nitrogen bases in the DNA of different species, scientists can infer how closely related two species are. The more similar the DNA sequences, the more closely related the species are. In most cases, evidence from DNA and protein structures has confirmed hypotheses based on fossils, embryos, and body structure.

A species is **extinct** if no members of that species are still alive. **Extinction is caused by a change in a species' environment. The members of the species may not have adaptations that allow them to survive and reproduce in the changed environment.** An environment's climate can change, too. Climate changes can destroy some organisms' habitats. Environmental change does not always lead to extinction. Some organisms in a species may have traits that help them survive in a changed environment.

Changes Over Time ▪ *Reading/Notetaking Guide*

Evolution of Species (pp. 217–222)

This section explains the factors that have contributed to the diversity of species, how new species form, how scientists infer evolutionary relationships among species, and what causes extinction.

Use Target Reading Skills

As you read, take notes on the main ideas and the important details. Consider the Key Concepts and Key Terms. Use the graphic organizer to help you take notes.

Recall Clues and Questions	Notes
What factors account for the diversity of species?	Factors include . . .

Changes Over Time ▪ *Reading/Notetaking Guide*

Evolution of Species *(continued)*

A Variety of Species (p. 218)

1. How have different environments produced different species?

   _____

   _____

2. What is a habitat?

   _____

3. List two ways that variations may occur.

   a. _____

   b. _____

4. Species with a lot of _____ in their gene pools can often adapt to changes in the environment because some individuals will have traits that let them survive in new conditions.

How Do New Species Form? (p. 219)

5. Is the following sentence true or false? When a group of individuals remains isolated from the rest of its species long enough to evolve different traits, a new species can form. _____

6. What are three ways that isolation can occur?

   _____

   _____

   _____

7. Why can isolation cause differences in species and possibly lead to a new species?

   _____

   _____

Changes Over Time • *Reading/Notetaking Guide*

Inferring Species Relationships (pp. 220–221)

8. Is the following sentence true or false? The more closely related species are, the more similar their DNA sequences. _____

9. What have scientists learned about the elephant shrew based on DNA evidence?

   _____

   _____

   _____

10. Circle the letter of each sentence that is true about evolutionary relationships of organisms.

    a. Scientists infer that species with similar body structures and development patterns inherited many of the same genes from a common ancestor.

    b. Scientists can compare protein structure to determine how closely two species are related.

    c. A branching tree shows how scientists think different groups of organisms are related.

    d. DNA evidence shows that giant pandas are more closely related to raccoons than to bears.

Changes Over Time ▪ *Reading/Notetaking Guide*

Evolution of Species *(continued)*

Extinction of Species *(pp. 221–222)*

11. If no members of a species are still alive, the species is

    _____.

12. Why can changes in a species' environment cause extinction?

    _____

    _____

13. Name two ways in which an environment can change.

    a. _____

    b. _____

14. Explain how a change in climate can lead to extinction.

    _____

    _____

    _____

15. Is the following sentence true or false? Environmental changes always
    lead to extinction because organisms do not have traits to help them
    survive the changes. _____

Classifying Organisms

Key Concepts

■ Why do biologists organize living things into groups?

■ What do the levels of classification indicate about the relationships between organisms?

■ What characteristics are used to classify organisms into domains and kingdoms?

Classification is the process of grouping things based on their similarities. **Biologists use classification to organize living things into groups so that the organisms are easier to study.** The scientific study of how living things are classified is called **taxonomy.** Taxonomy and evolution are closely related.

Carolus Linnaeus created a naming system for organisms called **binomial nomenclature,** in which each organism is given a two-part name. The first part of an organism's scientific name is its genus. A **genus** is a classification grouping that contains similar, closely related organisms. Together, the two words indicate a unique species.

Modern biologists classify organisms into eight levels: domain, kingdom, phylum, class, order, family, genus, and species. Organisms are grouped by their shared characteristics. **The more classification levels that two organisms share, the more characteristics they have in common.**

Today, a three-domain system of classification is commonly used. The three domains are Bacteria, Archaea, and Eukarya. Within the domains are kingdoms. **Organisms are placed into domains and kingdoms based on their cell type, their ability to make food, and the number of cells in their bodies.**

Members of the domain Bacteria are prokaryotes. **Prokaryotes** are organisms whose cells lack a nucleus. A nucleus is a dense area in a cell that contains nucleic acids. In prokaryotes, nucleic acids are scattered throughout the cell.

Like bacteria, members of the domain Archaea are unicellular prokaryotes. Archaea and bacteria are placed in different domains because there are important differences in the structure and chemical makeup of their cells.

Members of the domain Eukarya are **eukaryotes**—organisms with cells that contain nuclei. **Scientists classify organisms in the domain Eukarya into one of four kingdoms: protists, fungi, plants, or animals.**

Protists can be autotrophs or heterotrophs, unicellular or multicellular. Most fungi are multicellular eukaryotes. All fungi are heterotrophs.

Plants are all multicellular eukaryotes. In general, plants are autotrophs and feed almost all of the heterotrophs on land. All animals are multicellular eukaryotes. All animals are heterotrophs.

Changes Over Time · *Reading/Notetaking Guide*

Classifying Organisms (pp. 248–254)

This section describes how biologists organize living things, what the levels of classification indicate about the relationship between organisms, and what characteristics are used to classify organisms.

Use Target Reading Skills

As you read, take notes on the main ideas and important details. Use the graphic organizer below to take notes.

Recall Clues and Questions	Notes
Why do scientists classify living things?	Scientists classify living things because . . .

Why Do Scientists Classify? (p. 249)

1. The process of grouping things based on their similarities is called _____.

2. Why do biologists use classification?

   _____

   _____

3. The scientific study of how living things are classified is called _____.

4. How are taxonomy and evolution related?

   _____

5. In addition to classifying organisms, systematics tries to

   _____.

Changes Over Time ▪ *Reading/Notetaking Guide*

The Naming System of Linnaeus (pp. 250–251)

6. Is the following sentence true or false? Linnaeus placed organisms into groups based on their observable features. _____

7. In Linnaeus's naming system, called _____, each organism is given a two-part name.

8. A _____ is a classification grouping that contains similar, closely related organisms.

9. *Felis concolor* is the scientific name for mountain lions. To which genus do mountain lions belong? What is the species?
Genus: _____   Species: _____

10. Circle the letter of each sentence that is true about binomial nomenclature.

    a. A complete scientific name is written in italics.
    b. Scientific names contain Latin words because Latin was the language that most scientists used during Linnaeus's time.
    c. The genus name begins with a lowercase letter.
    d. Binomial nomenclature makes it easy for scientists to talk about organisms.

Levels of Classification? (pp. 251–252)

11. List the eight levels of classification used by modern biologists, in order, from the broadest level to the most specific level.

    _____

    _____

    _____

12. Is the following sentence true or false? The more classification levels that two organisms share, the more characteristics they have in common.

    _____

Changes Over Time · *Reading/Notetaking Guide*

Classifying Organisms *(continued)*

Domains and Kingdoms *(pp. 253–254)*

13. List the three domains of living things.

_____

_____

14. How are organisms placed in domains and kingdoms?

_____

_____

15. What are prokaryotes?

_____

16. Is the following sentence true or false? Some bacteria are heterotrophs, and some are autotrophs. _____

17. Why are archaea classified in their own domain?

_____

_____

18. Where can archaea be found?

_____

19. List the four kingdoms in the domain Eukarya.

_____

_____

20. A eukaryote is an organism with cells that contain _____.

21. Is the following sentence true or false? A protist is any eukaryote that can be classified as a plant, an animal, or a fungus.

_____

Chapter 7 Changes Over Time • *Section 5 Summary*

Branching Trees

Key Concepts

- How does a branching tree diagram show evolutionary relationships?

Groups of organisms with similar characteristics may be descended from a common ancestor. The more similar two groups are, the more recent their common ancestor probably is. A **branching tree diagram** shows probable evolutionary relationships among organisms. It also shows the order in which specific characteristics may have evolved. Branching tree diagrams begin at the base with common ancestors of all the organisms in the diagram.

A branching tree diagram shows evolutionary relationships by grouping organisms according to shared derived characteristics. A **shared derived characteristic** is usually a homologous structure, such as a backbone, that is shared by all organisms in a group. On a branching tree diagram, all the organisms above the label have the trait.

A branching tree diagram has groups within groups. Species within any group are more closely related to one another than to species not in the group.

Characteristics that appear lower on a branching tree probably developed before characteristics higher on the tree. For example, a branching tree diagram shows that during evolutionary history, animals with backbones appeared earlier than animals with both a backbone and four limbs.

To create a branching tree diagram, you begin with the common ancestor and continue moving up branches with groups that have one shared derived characteristic. This process continues until you get to the organism or group with the greatest number of shared derived characteristics. Branching tree diagrams show fossils as well as living organisms.

Branching Trees (pp. 255–257)

This section explains how branching tree diagrams show evolutionary relationships.

Use Target Reading Skills

As you read, create an outline of the main ideas and important details. Consider the Key Concept and Key Terms. Use the graphic organizer below to create your outline.

I. Shared Derived Characteristics

    A.

    B.

    C.

    D.

II.

    A.

    B.

    C.

Introduction (p. 255)

1. Groups of organisms with similar characteristics may be descended from a _____.

2. Is the following sentence true or false? The more similar two organisms are, the more distant their common ancestor probably is.

   _____

3. What does a branching tree diagram show?

   _____

   _____

Changes Over Time ▪ *Reading/Notetaking Guide*

Shared Derived Characteristics (p. 256)

4. How are organisms grouped on a branching tree diagram?

   _____

5. A shared derived characteristic is usually a _____,
   such as a backbone, that is shared by _____.

6. On a branching tree diagram, all organisms above the label
   _____.

7. Is the following sentence true or false? Species within a group are more
   closely related to one another than to species not in the group.

   _____

8. How does the order of characteristics on a branching tree diagram help
   demonstrate evolutionary history?

   _____

   _____

Constructing a Branching Tree (p. 257)

9. Where does a branching tree diagram begin, and where does it end?

   _____

   _____

10. Is the following sentence true or false? A branching tree diagram shows
    only living organisms. _____

Chapter 8 Earth's History · *Section 1 Summary*

The Rock Cycle

Key Concepts

- What is uniformitarianism?

- What is the rock cycle?

Geology is the study of the structure of planet Earth and the forces that make and shape Earth. In the late 1700s, a Scottish doctor and farmer named James Hutton studied the rocks and landscape around him. He watched streams cut through land in the process of **erosion.** Erosion occurs when running water, ice, or wind break down rocks and carry the pieces away. Hutton concluded that those same processes had occurred long ago.

Hutton's idea is called the principle of **uniformitarianism. The principle of uniformitarianism states that the geological processes that operate today also operated in the past.** Hutton observed that most geologic processes happen very slowly, and that they must have been at work a very long time to produce mountains and valleys. He concluded that Earth must be much older than people thought.

Geologists classify the rocks on Earth into three main groups— igneous, sedimentary, and metamorphic. Igneous rocks form when molten material beneath Earth's surfaces cools and hardens. **Sedimentary rock** is made of sediments that have been deposited and then pressed together to form solid rock. Most fossils are found in sedimentary rock. **Metamorphic rock** forms when an existing rock is changed by heat, pressure, or chemical reactions.

The **rock cycle** is a series of processes on and beneath Earth's surface that slowly change rocks from one kind to another. **Forces inside Earth and at the surface produce a rock cycle that builds, changes, and destroys rocks.** The rock cycle is a very slow process, taking place over millions of years.

One possible pathway through the rock cycle begins with **magma—** molten material beneath Earth's surface. As magma is forced toward the surface, it may form a volcanic mountain. Some of the magma hardens inside, forming volcanic rock. Some of the magma flows onto the surface as **lava.**

Over time, erosion wears away the mount, exposing the igneous rock. Chemicals, water, wind, and ice break the rock into tiny pieces and carry it away. Streams carry the particles of rock to the ocean, where they are deposited as sediment. Over millions of years, the layers build up and are cemented together. As more and more sediments pile up, the pressure increases. The rock becomes hot. Heat and pressure change the sedimentary rock into metamorphic rock.

The formation of metamorphic rock does not end the rock cycle. Forces inside Earth can push all three types of rock many kilometers beneath Earth's surface. The intense heat and pressure can melt the rock, and the cycle begins again.

Earth's History · *Reading/Notetaking Guide*

The Rock Cycle (pp. 240–243)

This section explains uniformitarianism and the rock cycle.

Use Target Reading Skills

As you read, create an outline to show the relationship between main ideas and supporting ideas. Use the headings, subheadings, and Key Concepts to help you complete the outline.

<table>
<tr><td colspan="2" align="center">The Rock Cycle</td></tr>
<tr><td>I. Hutton's Big Idea</td><td></td></tr>
<tr><td>   A.</td><td></td></tr>
<tr><td>   B.</td><td></td></tr>
<tr><td>   C.</td><td></td></tr>
<tr><td>   D.</td><td></td></tr>
<tr><td>   E.</td><td></td></tr>
<tr><td>   F.</td><td></td></tr>
<tr><td>II.</td><td></td></tr>
<tr><td>   A.</td><td></td></tr>
<tr><td>   B.</td><td></td></tr>
<tr><td>   C.</td><td></td></tr>
<tr><td>III.</td><td></td></tr>
<tr><td>   A.</td><td></td></tr>
<tr><td>   B.</td><td></td></tr>
<tr><td>   C.</td><td></td></tr>
<tr><td>   D.</td><td></td></tr>
<tr><td>   E.</td><td></td></tr>
<tr><td>   F.</td><td></td></tr>
<tr><td>   G.</td><td></td></tr>
<tr><td>   H.</td><td></td></tr>
</table>

Earth's History · *Reading/Notetaking Guide*

The Rock Cycle *(continued)*

Hutton's Big Idea (pp. 240–241)

Match the term with its definition.

Term

_____ **1.** geology

_____ **2.** erosion

Definition

a. process of running water, wind, or ice breaking down rocks and carrying the pieces away

b. study of the structure of Earth and the forces that shape it

3. What is the principle of uniformitarianism?

_____

_____

4. What did Hutton conclude based on his observations?

_____

Types of Rocks (p. 241)

Explain how the three main groups of rocks form.

a. _____

_____

b. _____

_____

c. _____

_____

Earth's History · *Reading/Notetaking Guide*

The Rock Cycle (pp. 242–243)

Complete the graphic organizer to show the rock cycle.

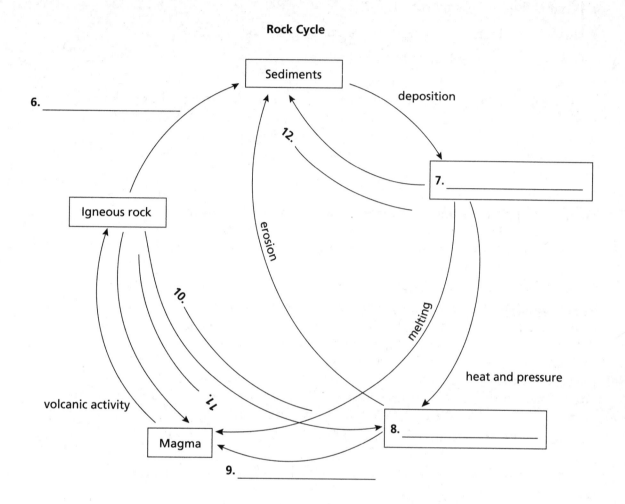

Rock Cycle

The Relative Age of Rocks

Key Concepts

- What is the law of superposition?

- How do geologists determine the relative age of rocks?

- How are index fossils useful to geologists?

The **relative age** of a rock is its age compared with the ages of other rocks. The **absolute age** of a rock is the number of years since the rock formed. The sediment that forms sedimentary rocks is deposited in flat layers. Over years, the sediment hardens and changes into sedimentary rock. These rock layers provide a record of Earth's geologic history.

It can be difficult to determine the absolute age of a rock. Geologists use the **law of superposition** to determine the relative ages of sedimentary rock layers. **According to the law of superposition, in horizontal sedimentary rock layers the oldest layer is at the bottom. Each higher layer is younger than the layers below it.**

There are other clues to the relative ages of rocks. **To determine relative age, geologists also study extrusions and intrusions of igneous rock, faults, and gaps in the geologic record.** Igneous rock forms when magma or lava hardens. Lava that hardens on the surface is called an **extrusion.** The rock layers below an extrusion are always older than the extrusion. Beneath the surface, magma may push into bodies of rock. There, the magma cools and hardens into a mass of igneous rock called an **intrusion.** An intrusion is always younger than the rock layers around and beneath it.

More clues come from the study of faults. A **fault** is a break in Earth's crust. A fault is always younger than the rock it cuts through. The surface where new rock layers meet a much older rock surface beneath them is called an **unconformity.** An unconformity is a gap in the geologic record. An unconformity shows where some rock layers have been lost because of erosion.

To date rock layers, geologists first give a relative age to a layer of rock at one location and then give the same age to matching layers at other locations. Certain fossils, called index fossils, help geologists match rock layers. To be useful as an **index fossil,** a fossil must be widely distributed and represent a type of organism that existed only briefly. **Index fossils are useful because they tell the relative ages of the rock layers in which they occur.** Geologists use particular types of organisms, such as ammonites, as index fossils. Ammonites were a group of hard-shelled animals that evolved in shallow seas more than 500 million years ago. They later became extinct. Ammonite fossils have been found in many different places.

Earth's History · *Reading/Notetaking Guide*

The Relative Age of Rocks (pp. 244–249)

This section explains how scientists determine whether a rock is older or younger than other rocks and how geologists use index fossils.

Use Target Reading Skills

As you read, take notes on the main ideas and supporting details. Consider the Key Concepts and Key Terms. Use the graphic organizer below to help you take notes.

Relative Age

Recall Clues and Questions	Notes
What does the position of rock layers reveal?	The position of rock layers shows . . .

Introduction (p. 244)

Match the term with its definition.

Term

_____ **1.** relative age

_____ **2.** absolute age

Definition

a. The number of years since the rock formed

b. The age of a rock compared to the ages of other rocks

Earth's History • *Reading/Notetaking Guide*

The Relative Age of Rocks (continued)

The Position of Rock Layers (p. 245)

3. According to the law of superposition, the _____ layer is at the bottom. Each higher layer is _____ than the layers below it.

4. Is the following sentence true or false? The deeper one travels into the Grand Canyon, the younger the rocks become. _____

Determining Relative Age (pp. 246–247)

5. Complete the table below about the clues that geologists use to find the relative ages of rocks.

Clues to the Relative Ages of Rocks		
Clue	**How It Forms**	**What Clue Tells Geologists**
Extrusion	a.	b.
Intrusion	c.	d.
Fault	e.	f.

6. A fault cuts through an extrusion. Which layer is older?_____

7. What is an unconformity?

_____

_____

Earth's History ▪ *Reading/Notetaking Guide*

8. Look carefully at Figure 6, "Unconformity," in your textbook. Then describe how an unconformity can form.

_____

_____

_____

_____

Using Fossils to Date Rocks (pp. 248–249)

9. Geologists use _____ fossils to match rock layers in different locations.

10. Circle the letter of each sentence that is true about index fossils.
    a. Index fossils must be found in many different areas.
    b. Index fossils must represent an organism that lived for a very long time.
    c. Index fossils tell the absolute ages of the rock layers in which they occur.
    d. A type of ammonite that is different from other ammonites is a useful index fossil.

Radioactive Dating

Key Concepts

- What happens during radioactive decay?

- What can be learned from radioactive dating?

- What is the probable age of Earth?

Rocks are a form of matter. All the matter you see, including rocks, is made of tiny particles called **atoms.** When all the atoms of a particular type of matter are the same, the matter is an **element.** Most elements are stable. They do not change under normal conditions. But some elements exist in forms that are unstable. Over time, these elements break down, or decay, by releasing particles and energy in a process called **radioactive decay.** These unstable elements are said to be radioactive. **During radioactive decay, the atoms of one element break down to form atoms of another element.**

Radioactive elements occur naturally in igneous rocks. For an igneous rock, its "birthday" is when it first hardens to become rock. As a radioactive element within the igneous rock decays, it changes into another element. Therefore, the composition of the rock changes slowly over time. The amount of the radioactive element decreases. But the amount of the new element increases. The rate of decay of each radioactive element is constant—it never changes. This rate of decay is the element's half-life. The **half-life** of a radioactive element is the time it takes for half of the radioactive atoms to decay.

Geologists use radioactive dating to determine the absolute ages of rocks. In radioactive dating, scientists first determine the amount of a radioactive element in a rock. Then they compare that amount with the amount of the stable element into which the radioactive element decays. Scientists often use potassium-40 to date rocks. This form of potassium decays to form the stable element argon-40 and has a half-life of 1.3 billion years. The long half-life of potassium-40 makes it useful in dating the most ancient rocks.

All plants and animals contain some carbon-14, a radioactive form of carbon. Carbon-14 is useful in dating materials from plants and animals that lived as far back as 50,000 years ago. Because carbon-14 has a half-life of only 5,730 years, it can't be used to date more ancient fossils or rocks.

Scientists have not found it easy to figure out the age of planet Earth. Earth is always changing through erosion and other processes. Most of the matter that made up early Earth has been destroyed or changed. Radioactive dating shows that the oldest rocks ever found on Earth are about 4.0 billion years old. But scientists hypothesize that Earth formed even earlier than that. Scientists have used moon rocks and meteorites to estimate the age of Earth. **Radioactive dating shows that the oldest moon rocks are about 4.6 billion years old. Scientists infer that Earth is only a little older than those moon rocks—roughly 4.6 billion years old.**

Earth's History • *Reading/Notetaking Guide*

Radioactive Dating (pp. 251–254)

This section describes what scientists can learn from radioactive dating and what the probable age of Earth is.

Use Target Reading Skills

As you read about radioactive dating, complete the graphic organizer by filling in the details.

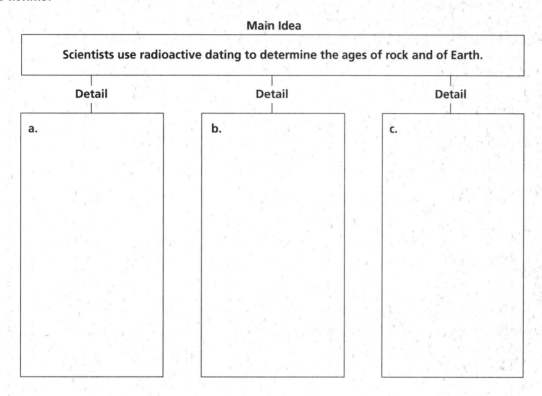

Main Idea

Scientists use radioactive dating to determine the ages of rock and of Earth.

Detail   **Detail**   **Detail**

a.   b.   c.

Radioactive Decay (p. 252)

1. A type of matter in which all the atoms making up the matter are the same is called a(n) _____.

2. Is the following sentence true or false? All elements decay over time.

   _____

3. What occurs during radioactive decay?

   _____

   _____

   _____

4. Circle the letter of the kind of rock for which radioactive dating works well.
      a. sedimentary   **c.** metamorphic
      b. igneous   **d.** layered

Earth's History ▪ *Reading/Notetaking Guide*

Radioactive Dating (continued)

5. How do scientists use the rate at which radioactive elements decay in rocks?

    _____

6. Circle the letter of each sentence that is true about radioactive decay.

    a. Over time, the amount of a radioactive element in igneous rock will increase.
    b. The rate of decay of each radioactive element is always changing.
    c. The rate of radioactive decay is an element's half-life.
    d. The half-life of a radioactive element is the time it takes for half of the radioactive atoms to decay.

Determining Absolute Ages (p. 253)

7. Is the following sentence true or false? Geologists use radioactive dating to find the absolute ages of rocks. _____

8. What two things must scientists measure to find the absolute age of a rock?

    a. _____

    _____

    b. _____

    _____

9. Is the following sentence true or false? By comparing the amount of the radioactive element with the amount of the stable element, scientists can determine the absolute age of a rock. _____

10. Complete the table to compare two different types of radioactive dating.

Elements Used in Radioactive Dating			
Element	**Decays to**	**Used for Dating**	**Half-Life**
Potassium-40	a.	b.	c.
Carbon-14	d.	e.	f.

    g. Suppose a geologist wants to determine the absolute age of an igneous rock. Based on the rock's place in the geologic record, the geologist thinks the rock might have formed about 400 million years ago. Would you use potassium-40 or carbon-14 to date the igneous rock? Explain your answer.

    _____

    _____

Earth's History · *Reading/Notetaking Guide*

11. Is the following sentence true or false? Carbon-14 can be used to date only organic materials that are less than about 50,000 years old. _____

How Old Is Earth? (p. 254)

12. Why have scientists had a difficult time determining the age of Earth?

_____

_____

13. Scientists have used _____ and _____ to estimate the age of Earth because they hypothesize that Earth formed before the oldest rocks found.

14. Why do scientists infer that Earth is roughly 4.6 billion years old?

_____

_____

_____

Movement of Earth's Plates

Key Concepts

■ How does the theory of plate tectonics explain the movement of Earth's landmasses?

■ How has the movement of Earth's plates affected organisms?

Earth's rocky outer layer consists of more than a dozen major pieces called **plates** that fit together like a jigsaw puzzle. Plate boundaries do not always lie along the edges of continents. Some lie under the ocean, and many have both continents and oceans on them.

Scientists use the concept of plates to explain how landmasses have changed over time. The **theory of plate tectonics** states that Earth's plates move slowly in various directions. The plates move, on average, about 5 centimeters per year. Some plates pull slowly away from each other, some plates push toward each other, and some plates slide past each other. **According to the theory of plate tectonics, Earth's landmasses have changed position over time because they are part of plates that are slowly moving.** About 300 million yeas ago, the continents were joined to form a supercontinent. The very slow movement of continents is called **continental drift.**

Over time, the movement of Earth's plates has affected the evolution of living things. **As Earth's plates have moved, landmasses have changed their locations. These changes have affected where different kinds of organisms, past and present, are located.** As the continents move, their climates may change. As the climate changes, so do the kinds of organisms that live there.

The fossils of the dinosaur *Brachiosaurus* have been found iin Europe, Africa, and North America. The location of these fossils suggests that Europe, Africa, and North America were once joined.

Continental drift has also affected organisms that are alive today. When populations of organisms become widely separated, their genetic makeup may change in different ways. Therefore, the separated populations often evolved differently.

Earth's History · *Reading/Notetaking Guide*

Movement of Earth's Plates (pp. 255–257)

This section explains the movement of Earth's landmasses and how the movement of Earth's plates has affected organisms.

Use Target Reading Skills

As you read, identify the effects of the movement of Earth's plates. Write them in the graphic organizer below.

Effects

Cause

Plate movement

a.

b.

c.

Earth's Plates (p. 256)

1. Earth's rocky outer layer consists of more than a dozen _____ that fit together.

2. What is the theory of plate tectonics?

   _____

   _____

3. What does the theory of plate tectonics help explain?

   _____

4. What three ways do plates move?

   a. _____

   b. _____

   c. _____

5. Circle the letter of each sentence that is true about Earth's plates.

   a. On average, Earth's plates move about 5 meters each year.

   b. About 300 million years ago, all the continents joined together to form Pangaea.

   c. The plate boundaries lie along the edges of the continents.

   d. Continental drift is the very slow movement of continents.

Earth's History ▪ *Reading/Notetaking Guide*

Movement of Earth's Plates *(continued)*

Plate Movement and Organisms (pp. 256–257)

6. How has the movement of Earth's plates affected the evolution of living things?

   _____

   _____

   _____

7. Is the following sentence true or false? Millions of years ago, North America's climate was warm and tropical because the North American plate was much closer to the equator.

   _____

8. The location of _____ suggests that Europe, Africa, and North America were once joined.

9. How has continental drift affected organisms that are alive today?

   _____

   _____

Chapter 8 Earth's History ▪ *Section 5 Summary*

The Geologic Time Scale

Key Concepts

■ Why is the geologic time scale used to show Earth's history?

■ What were early Precambrian organisms like?

■ What were the major events of the Paleozoic, Mesozoic, and Cenozoic Eras?

Because the time span of Earth's past is so great, geologists use the geologic time scale to show Earth's history. The **geologic time scale** is a record of the life forms and geologic events in Earth's history.

Geologic time begins with a long span of time called Precambrian Time. After Precambrian Time, the basic units of the geologic time scale are eras and periods.

Scientist cannot pinpoint when or where life began. **But scientists have found fossils of single-celled organisms in rocks that formed about 3.5 billion years ago. These earliest life forms were probably similar to present-day bacteria.**

During the Cambrian Period, life took a big leap forward. **At the beginning of the Paleozoic Era, a great number of kinds of organisms evolved.** Many were animals without backbones, or **invertebrates. During this time, jawless fishes evolved. Jawless fishes were the first vertebrates.** A **vertebrate** is an animal with a backbone. **During the Devonian Period, animals began to invade the land.** Small reptiles developed during the Carboniferous Period.

At the end of the Paleozoic Era, many kinds of organisms died out. This was a **mass extinction,** in which many types of living things became extinct at the same time. **The mass extinction at the end of the Paleozoic Era affected both plants and animals, on land and in the seas.** Scientists hypothesize that climate change resulting from continental drift may have caused this mass extinction. **During the Permian Period, about 260 million years ago, Earth's continents moved together to form a great landmass, or supercontinent, called Pangaea.** Plants and animals that included fish, insects, reptiles, and cone-bearing plants called conifers survived the mass extinction.

Reptiles were so successful during the Mesozoic Era that this time is often called the Age of Reptiles. About 225 million years ago, the first dinosaurs appeared. Mammals also first appeared during the Triassic Period.

At the close of the Cretaceous Period, about 65 million years ago, another mass extinction occurred. Scientists hypothesize that this mass extinction occurred when an object from space struck Earth.

The extinction of dinosaurs created an opportunity for mammals. During the Cenozoic Era, mammals evolved to live in many different environments. Earth's climate cooled, causing a series of ice ages during the Quaternary Period.

Earth's History ▪ *Reading/Notetaking Guide*

The Geologic Time Scale (pp. 258–269)

This section tells why the geologic time scale is used to show Earth's history, and what the organisms were like and the major events that happened in the different periods and eras.

Use Target Reading Skills

As you read, create an outline to show the relationships between main ideas and supporting ideas. Use the headings, subheadings, and Key Concepts to help you complete the outline.

The Geologic Time Scale

I. The Geologic Time Scale
    A.
    B.
    C.
    D.
    E.
    F.
 	
II. The Paleozoic Era
    A.
    B.
    C.
    D.
    E.
    F.
    G.
    H.
    I.
 	
III. The Mesozoic Era
    A.
    B.
    C.
    D.
    E.
 	
IV. The Cenozoic Era
    A.
    B.
    C.
    D.
    E.
    F.

Earth's History ▪ *Reading/Notetaking Guide*

The Geologic Time Scale (pp. 258–260)

1. Is the following sentence true or false? Using months, years, and centuries is a very useful way of thinking about Earth's long history.

   _____

2. What is the geologic time scale?

   _____

   _____

   _____

3. Geologic time begins _____ with a long span of time called

   _____ .

4. The basic units of the geologic time scale are **a.** _____ and

   b. _____ .

5. Scientists hypothesize that all forms of life on Earth arose from

   _____ that formed about _____ .

6. How do scientists believe the ozone layer formed, and what did the ozone layer allow for?

   _____

   _____

   _____

   _____

   _____

Earth's History • *Reading/Notetaking Guide*

The Geologic Time Scale *(continued)*

The Paleozoic Era *(pp. 261–265)*

7. What happened during the Cambrian Explosion?

_____

_____

8. Complete the flowchart to show how living things evolved during the Paleozoic Era.

The Paleozoic Era

During the Silurian Period, simple **a.** _____ began to grow on land in damp areas.

↓

During the Devonian Period, **b.** _____, animals that live part of their life on land and part of their life in water, evolved.

↓

During the Carboniferous Period, **c.** _____, which have scaly skin and lay eggs with tough, leathery shells, first developed.

↓

At the end of the Paleozoic Era, **d.** _____ occurred, which means that many types of living things died out at the same time.

e. How did the event in the first box help lead to animals' moving from water to land?

_____

_____

Earth's History ▪ *Reading/Notetaking Guide*

9. Is the following sentence true or false? During the Cambrian Period, all animals lived in the sea. _____

10. An animal with a backbone is called a(n) _____.

11. What were the first vertebrates to evolve?

_____

_____

12. What is a mass extinction?

_____

_____

13. What is one theory for the mass extinction at the end of the Paleozoic Era?

_____

_____

14. What happened to Earth's continents during the Permian Period?

_____

_____

_____

Earth's History • *Reading/Notetaking Guide*

The Geologic Time Scale *(continued)*

15. Is the following sentence true or false? The formation of Pangaea caused the climate on Earth to change. _____

The Mesozoic Era (pp. 266–267)

16. Circle the letter of the type of living thing that was most successful during the Mesozoic Era.

    a. insects   **c.** conifers
    b. fish   **d.** reptiles

17. _____, the first warm-blooded vertebrates that fed their young with milk, appeared during the Triassic Period.

18. One of the first birds appeared in the _____ Period of the Mesozoic Era.

19. Circle the letter of each sentence that is true about living things in the Cretaceous Period.

    a. Reptiles were the dominant vetebrates.
    b. Flying reptiles were better adapted to flying than birds.
    c. Turtles and crocodiles became extinct.
    d. Flowering plants evolved.

20. What is one hypothesis for the mass extinction at the end of the Cretaceous Period?

_____

_____

_____

_____

The Cenozoic Era (pp. 268–269)

21. Why didn't mammals evolve more during the Mesozoic Era?

_____

_____

_____

22. Is the following sentence true or false? Whales and dolphins are all mammals that evolved in the oceans during the Tertiary Period. _____

23. How did Earth's climate change in the Quaternary Period?

_____

_____

_____

24. Human ancestors first appeared in the _____ Period.

Viruses

Key Concepts

- How are viruses like organisms?
- What is the structure of a virus?
- How do viruses multiply?
- How can you treat a viral disease?

A **virus** is a tiny, nonliving particle that enters and then reproduces inside a living cell. Biologists consider viruses to be nonliving because viruses are not cells and do not have the characteristics of organisms. **The only way in which viruses are like organisms is that they can multiply.**

Although viruses can multiply, they do so differently than organisms. Viruses can multiply only when they are inside a living cell. The organism that a virus enters and multiplies inside is called a host. A **host** is an organism that provides a source of energy for a virus or another organism. Organisms that live on or in a host and cause it harm are called **parasites.** Most viruses are like parasites because they destroy their host cells.

Viruses are smaller than cells and vary in shape and size. Viruses can be round, or shaped like rods, bricks, threads, or bullets. Some viruses, such as bacteriophages, have complex, robot-like shapes. A **bacteriophage** is a virus that infects bacteria.

All viruses have two basic parts: a protein coat that protects the virus and an inner core made of genetic material. Some viruses are surrounded by an additional membrane envelope. Each virus contains unique proteins on its outer surface. The shape of these proteins allows the virus to attach to, or lock onto, only certain host cells.

After a virus attaches to a host cell, it enters the cell. **Once inside a cell, a virus's genetic material takes over many of the cell's functions. It instructs the cell to produce the virus's proteins and genetic material. These proteins and genetic material then assemble into new viruses.**

An active virus immediately takes over the cell's functions, and the cell quickly begins to produce the virus's proteins and genetic material. These parts are assembled into new viruses. When it is full of new viruses, the host cell bursts open and releases the new viruses as it dies.

When a hidden virus enters a host cell, the virus's genetic material becomes part of the cell's genetic material. The virus's genetic material may stay inactive for a long time. Then, the virus's genetic material suddenly becomes active and takes over the cell's functions and replicates. Once the host cell is full of new viruses, it bursts open to release them.

Viral diseases can be spread in various ways. There are currently no cures for viral diseases. **Resting, drinking plenty of fluids, and eating well-balanced meals may be all you can do while you recover from a viral disease.** Vaccines also help prevent the spread of viral diseases. A **vaccine** is a substance introduced into the body to stimulate the production of chemicals that destroy specific disease-causing viruses and organisms.

Viruses, Bacteria, Protists, and Fungi ▪ *Reading/Notetaking Guide*

Viruses (pp. 214–219)

This section describes what viruses are, how they multiply, and how you can treat a viral disease.

Use Target Reading Skills

Complete the Venn diagram to compare and contrast active viruses and hidden viruses. Consider what they are, how they multiply, and how they take over the host cell.

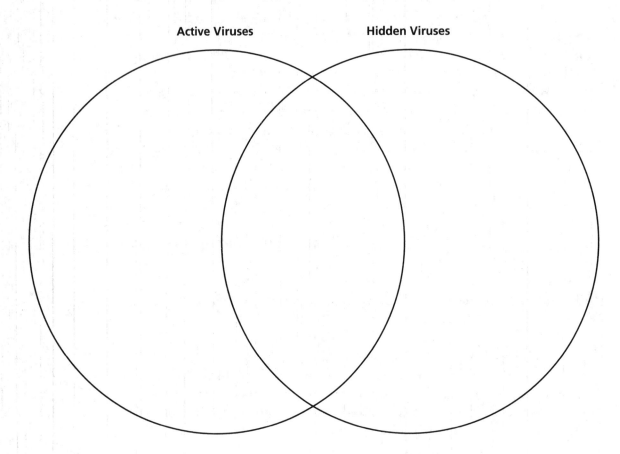

Active Viruses   Hidden Viruses

Viruses, Bacteria, Protists, and Fungi • *Reading/Notetaking Guide*

What Is a Virus? (pp. 214–215)

1. Why do biologists consider viruses to be nonliving?

   _____

   _____

   _____

2. Is the following sentence true or false? Viruses multiply the same way as other organisms. _____

3. Circle the name of a living thing that provides energy for a virus or an organism.

   a. parasite
   b. host
   c. bacteriophage
   d. particle

4. Viruses act like _____ because they destroy the cells in which they multiply.

5. Is the following sentence true or false? Each virus can enter only a few types of cells in a few specific species. _____

6. Is the following sentence true or false? All viruses have the same shape.

   _____

7. A virus that infects bacteria is called a(n) _____.

8. Is the following sentence true or false? Viruses are much smaller than bacteria. _____

9. Circle the letter of each sentence that is true about viruses.

   a. They are larger than cells.
   b. They need to be inside a living cell in order to reproduce.
   c. They contain genetic material.
   d. They are all round in shape.

10. Label the two basic parts of a virus in this diagram.

a. _____   b. _____

Viruses *(continued)*

11. Is the following sentence true or false? Some viruses are surrounded by an outer membrane envelope. _____

12. What are two functions of a virus's protein coat?

    a. _____

    b. _____

13. Is the following sentence true or false? The shape of the proteins allows the virus's coat to attach to only certain cells in the host.

    _____

How Viruses Multiply (pp. 216–217)

Match the kind of virus with the way it multiplies in a cell. Viruses may be used more than once.

How It Multiplies

_____ **14.** The virus's genetic material becomes part of the cell's genetic material.

_____ **15.** The virus immediately begins to multiply after entering the cell.

_____ **16.** The virus stays inactive for a long time.

Viruses

a. active virus

b. hidden virus

17. Is the following sentence true or false? When the virus is active, the cell makes the virus's proteins and genetic material and new viruses are made. _____

18. What happens when a cell is full of new viruses?

    _____

    _____

Viruses, Bacteria, Protists, and Fungi • *Reading/Notetaking Guide*

Viruses and Disease (pp. 218–219)

19. Is the following sentence true or false? Viruses can cause diseases only in humans. _____

20. List at least two ways that viral diseases can be spread.

_____

_____

21. What is often the best treatment for viral infections?

_____

_____

_____

22. A _____ is a substance introduced into the body to stimulate the production of chemicals that destroy specific disease-causing viruses and organisms.

23. How does a vaccine work?

_____

_____

24. What are some other ways to protect against viral diseases?

_____

_____

_____

Chapter 9 Viruses, Bacteria, Protists, and Fungi • *Section 2 Summary*

Bacteria

Key Concepts

- How do the cells of bacteria differ from those of eukaryotes?

- What do bacteria need to survive?

- Under what conditions do bacteria thrive and reproduce?

- What positive roles do bacteria play in people's lives?

Bacteria are single-celled organisms. **Bacteria are prokaryotes. The genetic material in their cells is not contained in a nucleus.** Most bacterial cells have one of three basic shapes: spherical, rodlike, or spiral.

Most bacterial cells are surrounded by a rigid cell wall that helps to protect the cell. Inside the cell wall is the cell membrane. Inside the cytoplasm are ribosomes and the cell's genetic material. Some bacteria have flagella. A **flagellum** is a long, whiplike structure that helps a cell to move.

All bacteria need certain things to survive. **Bacteria must have a source of food and a way of breaking down the food to release its energy.** Some bacteria are autotrophs and make their own food. Others are heterotrophs that obtain food by consuming other organisms or the food that organisms make. Like all organisms, bacteria need a constant supply of energy. This energy comes from breaking down food in the process of respiration.

When bacteria have plenty of food, the right temperature, and other suitable conditions, they thrive and reproduce frequently. Bacteria reproduce by **binary fission,** a process in which one cell divides to form two identical cells. Binary fission is a form of asexual reproduction. **Asexual reproduction** is a reproductive process that involves only one parent and produces offspring that are identical to the parent. Some bacteria may at times undergo a form of sexual reproduction. **Sexual reproduction** involves two parents who combine their genetic material to produce a new organism that differs from both parents. During a process called **conjugation,** one bacterium transfers some of its genetic material into another. After the transfer, the cells separate. The result is bacteria with new combinations of genetic material.

Many bacteria can survive harsh conditions by forming endospores. An **endospore** is a small, rounded, thick-walled, resting cell that forms inside a bacterial cell.

Some bacteria cause diseases and other harmful conditions. However, most bacteria are either harmless or helpful to people. **Bacteria are involved in oxygen and food production, environmental recycling and cleanup, and health maintainance and medicine production.** Helpful bacteria produce foods; however, some bacteria cause food to spoil. One method to slow down food spoilage is **pasteurization,** where food is heated to a temperature that is high enough to kill most harmful bacteria without changing the taste of the food. Heterotrophic bacteria in the soil break down materials for reuse. These bacteria are **decomposers**—organisms that break down large chemicals in dead organisms into small chemicals. Many bacteria living in your body actually keep you healthy.

Viruses, Bacteria, Protists, and Fungi • *Reading/Notetaking Guide*

Bacteria (pp. 221–229)

This section explains what bacteria are, how they reproduce, and their role in nature.

Use Target Reading Skills

Complete the Venn diagram to compare and contrast bacteria and viruses.

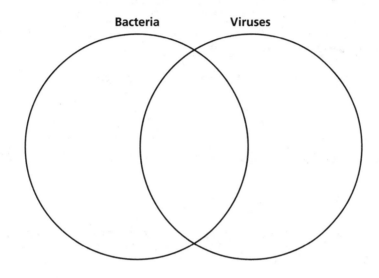

Bacteria   **Viruses**

The Bacterial Cell (pp. 221–222)

1. Bacteria are _____. The genetic material in their cells is not contained in a nucleus.

2. A bacterial cell lacks a _____ and many other structures like _____ and _____ that are found in the cells of eukaryotes.

3. Circle the letter of the cell structure that helps a bacterium to move.

    a. cell wall   b. cytoplasm
    c. ribosome   d. flagellum

4. Label the parts of a bacterial cell in this diagram.

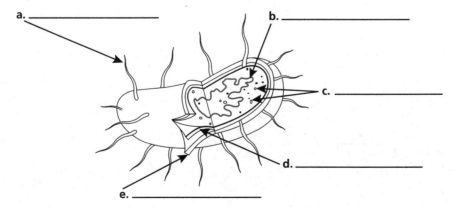

a. _____   b. _____

c. _____

d. _____

e. _____

Viruses, Bacteria, Protists, and Fungi • *Reading/Notetaking Guide*

Bacteria *(continued)*

5. Is the following sentence true or false? Bacteria that do not have flagella are never moved from one place to another. _____

6. What are the three basic shapes of bacterial cells?

    a. _____ b. _____

    c. _____

Obtaining Food and Energy *(p. 223)*

7. List the two ways in which autotrophic bacteria make food.

    a. _____

    b. _____

8. How do heterotrophic bacteria get food?

    _____

    _____

9. Is the following sentence true or false? All bacteria must use oxygen to break down food for energy. _____

Reproduction *(pp. 224–225)*

10. Complete the table below about reproduction in bacteria.

Reproduction in Bacteria

	Asexual Reproduction	Sexual Reproduction
Name of Process		
Number of Parents		
What Occurs in Process		
Result of Process		

Viruses, Bacteria, Protists, and Fungi ▪ *Reading/Notetaking Guide*

11. When do bacteria form endospores?

_____

_____

The Role of Bacteria in Nature (pp. 226–229)

12. Circle the letter of each sentence that is true about bacteria.

    a. All bacteria are harmful and cause disease.

    b. Some bacteria release oxygen into the air.

    c. Bacteria help produce foods such as cheese, apple cider, and sauerkraut.

    d. Bacteria do not cause food to spoil.

13. What is pasteurization?

_____

_____

14. Soil bacteria that break down large chemicals in dead organisms into small chemicals are called _____.

15. Is the following sentence true or false? Bacteria can be used to clean up oil spills and gasoline leaks. _____

16. List three ways that bacteria in your digestive system are helpful to you.

    a. _____

    b. _____

    c. _____

17. How do bacteria help people with diabetes?

_____

_____

Chapter 9 Viruses, Bacteria, Protists, and Fungi • *Section 3 Summary*

Protists

Key Concepts

- What are the characteristics of animal-like, plantlike, and funguslike protists?

- How do algae vary in organization, structure, and function?

The protist kingdom is very diverse. All **protists** are eukaryotes that cannot be classified as animals, plants, or fungi. All live in moist surroundings. Most are unicellular, but some are multicellular. Some are heterotrophs, some are autotrophs, and some are both. Protists can be divided into three categories: animal-like, plantlike, and funguslike protists.

Like animals, animal-like protists are heterotrophs, and most are able to move from place to place to obtain food. Animal-like protists, also called **protozoans,** can be divided into four types: sarcodines, ciliates, flagellates, and parasites. Sarcodines move and feed by using **pseudopods,** which are temporary bulges of the cell. Protozoans that live in fresh water, such as amoebas, have a **contractile vacuole,** which collects the extra water and expels it from the cell. Ciliates have structures called **cilia,** which are hairlike projections that move with a wavelike motion. Flagellates move using whiplike flagella. Some flagellates live inside the bodies of other organisms in a state of symbiosis. **Symbiosis** is a close relationship between two species in which at least one of the species benefits. Sometimes, flagellates harm their hosts. In other cases, their relationship is one of **mutualism,** in which both partners benefit. Protozoans that are parasites feed on their hosts' cells and body fluids.

Plantlike protists are called **algae. Algae vary greatly in cell organization, structure, and function. Some algae are unicellular. Others are multicellular with differentiated tissues and organs. Still others are groups of unicellular organisms that live together in colonies.** Plantlike protists include diatoms, dinoflagellates, euglenoids, red algae, green algae, and brown algae. Diatoms are a food source for heterotrophs in water. Dinoflagellates are covered by stiff plates and move using two flagella. Euglenoids can be heterotrophs when sunlight is not available. Red algae are multicellular seaweeds. Green algae live in fresh water, salt water, and moist places on land. Green algae are very closely related to plants that live on land. Brown algae are multicellular and have the most complex structure of all algae.

Like fungi, funguslike protists are heterotrophs, have cell walls, and use spores to reproduce. Spores are tiny cells that are able to grow into new organisms. All funguslike protists are able to move at some point in their lives. The three types of funguslike protists are slime molds, water molds, and downy mildews. Slime molds live in moist soil and on decaying plants. Water molds and downy mildews grow in water or moist places.

Viruses, Bacteria, Protists, and Fungi • *Reading/Notetaking Guide*

Protists (pp. 230–239)

This section describes the characteristics of protists and how algae vary in organization, structure, and function.

Use Target Reading Skills

As you read, make an outline about protists that you can use for review. Use the red section headings for the main topics and blue headings for the subtopics.

Protists

I. What is a protist?
II. Animal-like protists
    A. Protozoans with pseudopods
    B.
    C.
    D.
III.
    A.
    B.
    C.
    D.
    E.
    F.
IV.
    A.
    B.
    C.

What Is a Protist? (p. 231)

1. Circle the letter of each sentence that is true about protists.

    a. All protists are eukaryotes that cannot be classified as animals, plants, or fungi.

    b. All protists live in dry surroundings.

    c. All protists are unicellular.

    d. Some protists are heterotrophs, some are autotrophs, and some are both.

Name _____ Date _____ Class _____

Protists (continued)

2. List the three categories into which scientists group protists.

    a. _____

    b. _____

    c. _____

Animal-Like Protists (pp. 231–234)

3. Circle the letter of each characteristic that animal-like protists share with animals.

    a. autotroph
    c. movement

    b. heterotroph
    d. unicellular

4. Another name for an animal-like protist is _____.

5. Describe how a sarcodine, such as an amoeba, gets food.

    _____

    _____

    _____

6. Circle the letter of the cell part in an ameoba that removes excess water.

    a. pseudopod
    b. cilia
    c. contractile vacuole
    d. cell membrane

7. Is the following sentence true or false? Paramecia have more than one nucleus. _____

Match the animal-like protist with the cell part it uses for movement.

Protist

____ 8. amoeba

____ 9. paramecium

____ 10. flagellate

Cell Part

a. cilia

b. flagella

c. pseudopods

11. Is the following sentence true or false? Flagellates living in symbiosis always harm the animal in which they live. _____

Viruses, Bacteria, Protists, and Fungi ▪ *Reading/Notetaking Guide*

12. Protozoans that are _____ feed on the cells and body fluids of their hosts.

13. Is the following sentence true or false? Protozoans that are parasites never have more than one host. _____

Plantlike Protists (pp. 235–237)

14. Plantlike protists are commonly called _____.

15. Like plants, plantlike protists are _____; most are able to use the sun's energy to make their own food.

16. Complete this table about the different types of plantlike protists.

Characteristics of Plantlike Protists

Type	Unicellular or Multicellular	Characteristics
Diatoms		
Dinoflagellates		
Euglenoids		
Red Algae		
Green Algae		
Brown Algae		

Viruses, Bacteria, Protists, and Fungi ▪ *Reading/Notetaking Guide*

Protists *(continued)*

Funguslike Protists (pp. 238–239)

17. Circle the letter of each sentence that is true about funguslike protists.

    a. Funguslike protists are heterotrophs.

    b. Funguslike protists do not have cell walls.

    c. Funguslike protists use spores to reproduce.

    d. Funguslike protists never move during their lives.

18. List the three types of funguslike protists.

    a. _____

    b. _____

    c. _____

19. Where do most water molds and downy mildews live? _____
_____

20. Circle the letter of each place where slime molds live.

    a. dry soil   **b.** moist soil

    c. decaying plants   **d.** in animals

Chapter 9 Viruses, Bacteria, Protists, and Fungi • *Section 4 Summary*

Fungi

Key Concepts

- What characteristics do fungi share?
- How do fungi reproduce?
- What roles do fungi play in nature?

Most **fungi** share several important characteristics: **Fungi are eukaryotes that have cell walls, are heterotrophs that feed by absorbing their food, and use spores to reproduce.** Fungi also need moist, warm places in which to grow. They vary in size from unicellular yeasts to multicellular mushrooms.

Hyphae (singular: hypha) are branching, threadlike tubes that make up the bodies of multicellular fungi. What a fungus looks like depends on the arrangement of its hyphae.

Fungi are heterotrophs, but they do not take food into their bodies in the way that animals do. First, the fungus grows hyphae into a food source. Then digestive chemicals ooze from the hyphae into the food. The digestive chemicals break down the food into small substances that can be absorbed by the hyphae. Some fungi feed on the remains of dead organisms. Others are parasites that break down the chemicals in living organisms.

Fungi usually reproduce by making spores. The lightweight spores are surrounded by a protective covering and can be carried easily through the air or water to new sites. Fungi produce spores in reproductive structures called **fruiting bodies.** Unicellular yeasts use a form of asexual reproduction called **budding.** In budding, a small cell grows from the body of a large, well-fed cell. Asexual reproduction results in fungi that are genetically identical to the parent. Fungi may reproduce sexually, especially when conditions become less favorable. This occurs when the hyphae of two fungi grow together and new genetic material is exchanged. In time, a new reproductive structure grows from the joined hyphae and produces spores. These spores develop into fungi genetically different from either parent. Three major groups of fungi include sac fungi, club fungi, and zygote fungi. The groups are named for the appearance of their reproductive structures.

Fungi play important roles as decomposers and recyclers on Earth. Many fungi provide foods for people. Some fungi cause disease while others fight disease. Still other fungi live in symbiosis with other organisms. Fungi break down the chemicals in dead organisms. This returns nutrients to the soil. Yeasts are important in the preparation of foods such as bread. People also eat some types of fungi, such as mushrooms. Many fungi cause disease in crops and in humans. Others, such as *Penicillium*, make useful substances that kill bacteria. The hyphae of some fungi grow among the roots of plants. The hyphae help the plant absorb more water and nutrients from the soil. In return, the fungus feeds on extra food the plant makes. A **lichen** consists of a fungus living in a mutualistic relationship with either algae or autotrophic bacteria.

Name _____ Date _____ Class _____

Fungi (pp. 240–245)

This section explains what fungi are, how they get food, and their role in the environment.

Use Target Reading Skills

Complete the Venn diagram to compare and contrast fungi and funguslike protists.

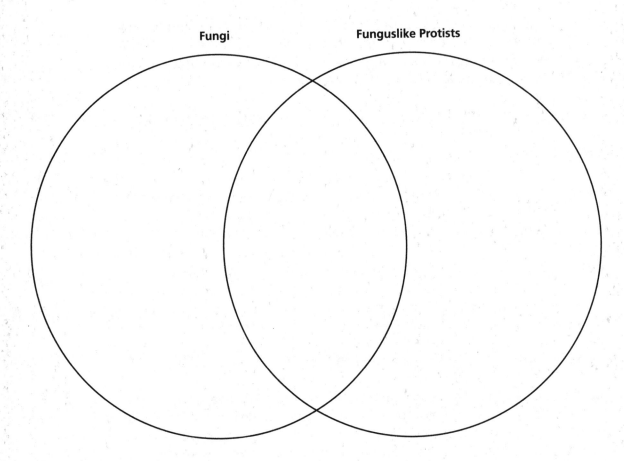

Fungi   Funguslike Protists

What Are Fungi? (pp. 240–241)

1. Circle the letter of each sentence that is true about fungi.

     a. All fungi have cell walls.

     b. They are eukaryotes.

     c. They use spores to reproduce.

     d. They are autotrophs.

2. What are three examples of fungi?

_____

_____

Viruses, Bacteria, Protists, and Fungi • *Reading/Notetaking Guide*

3. The cells of fungi are arranged in branching, threadlike tubes called _____.

4. Is the following sentence true or false? Fuzzy-looking molds that grow on food have hyphae that are packed tightly together. _____

5. Identify the structures of the mushroom shown here.

a. _____

b. _____

c. _____

d. _____

e. _____

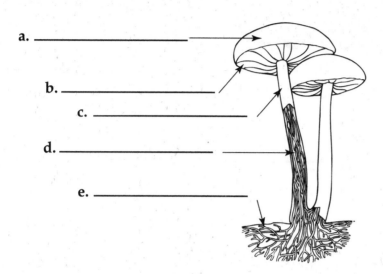

6. Is the following sentence true or false? What a fungus looks like depends on how its hyphae are arranged. _____

7. Describe the process by which a fungus feeds.

_____

_____

_____

_____

_____

Reproduction in Fungi (p. 242)

8. Most fungi reproduce by making _____ that are surrounded by a protective covering and can be _____

_____.

9. Fungi produce spores in reproductive structures called

_____.

10. Yeast cells reproduce asexually in a process called _____.

11. Is the following sentence true or false? Fungi reproduce sexually when growing conditions become unfavorable. _____

Viruses, Bacteria, Protists, and Fungi ▪ *Reading/Notetaking Guide*

Fungi (continued)

12. What are the three major groups of fungi?

    a. _____ b. _____

    c. _____

The Role of Fungi in Nature (pp. 243–245)

13. What types of fungi are important food sources?

    _____

14. Since the discovery of _____, many antibiotics
    have been isolated from both _____ and

    _____.

15. Fungi that are _____ break down the chemicals in
    dead organisms.

16. Is the following sentence true or false? The fungi that cause some
    diseases can spread easily because they produce spores at the site of the
    infection. _____

17. How do some fungi help plants grow larger and healthier?

    _____

    _____

    _____

    _____

18. An organism that consists of a fungus and either algae or autotrophic
    bacteria that live together in a mutualistic relationship is a(n)
    _____. The fungus provides the algae or
    autotrophic bacteria with _____.
    The algae or autotrophic bacteria provide the fungus with

    _____.

19. Why are lichens often called "pioneer" organisms?

    _____

    _____

Chapter 10 Structure and Function of Plants · *Section 1 Summary*

The Plant Kingdom

Key Concepts

- What characteristics do all plants share?
- What do plants need to live successfully on land?
- How do nonvascular plants and vascular plants differ?
- What are the different stages of a plant's life cycle?

Nearly all plants are autotrophs, organisms that produce their own food. All plants are eukaryotes that contain many cells. In addition, all plant cells are surrounded by cell walls. Plant cells contain chloroplasts and vacuoles. Like many other multicellular organisms, plants have levels of organization for structure and function. Tissues work together to form organs—leaves, stems, and roots. A plant has two organ systems. Above ground is the shoot system, which includes stems, leaves, and buds. Below ground is the root system, which absorbs water and nutrients and anchors the plant in the soil.

Most plants live on land. **To survive on land, plants have structures that allow them to obtain water and other nutrients from their surroundings, retain water, transport materials within their bodies, support their bodies, and reproduce.** Most plants have a waxy, waterproof layer covering their leaves called a **cuticle.** The cuticle helps keep water inside a plant cell rather than let it evaporate into the air. Some plants have **vascular tissue,** a system of tubelike structures inside the plant through which food, minerals, and water move. All plants undergo sexual reproduction that involves fertilization, the joining of a sperm cell with an egg cell. The fertilized egg is called a **zygote.**

Scientists informally group plants into two major groups— nonvascular and vascular plants. Nonvascular plants do not have a well-developed system of tubes for transporting water and other materials. They grow low to the ground and obtain water directly from their surroundings. **Vascular plants** have well-developed vascular tissue to transport and move materials quickly and efficiently throughout the plant's body. Vascular tissue also provides strength, stability, and support to a plant. Thus, vascular plants are able to grow quite tall.

Biologists infer that ancient green algae were the ancestors of today's land plants because land plants and green algae contain the same forms of chlorophyll. Comparison of genetic material shows that plants and green algae are very closely related.

Plants have complex life cycles that include two stages, the sporophyte stage and the gametophyte stage. In the **sporophyte** stage, the plant produces spores, tiny cells that can grow into new organisms. A spore develops into the plant's other stage, called the **gametophyte** stage. In the gametophyte stage, the plant produces two kinds of sex cells: sperm cells and egg cells. A sperm cell and egg cell join to form a zygote, which then develops into a sporophyte.

Structure and Function of Plants ▪ *Reading/Notetaking Guide*

The Plant Kingdom (pp. 352–359)

This section explains the features that plants share. It also describes what plants need to survive and how they reproduce.

Use Target Reading Skills

Use the cycle diagram to show the life cycle of a plant, including the sporophyte stage and the gametophyte stage.

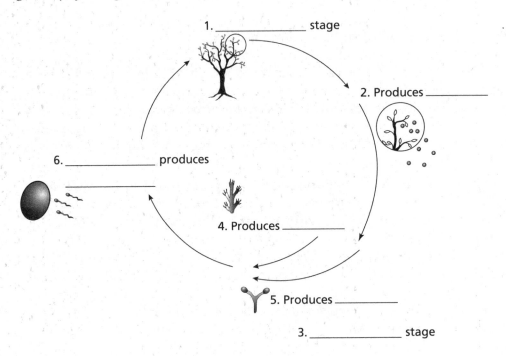

1. _____ stage

2. Produces _____

6. _____ produces

4. Produces _____

5. Produces _____

3. _____ stage

Structure and Function of Plants ▪ *Reading/Notetaking Guide*

What Is a Plant? (pp. 352–353)

1. Circle the letter of each characteristic that plants share.

   a. heterotroph
   b. autotroph
   c. prokaryote
   d. eukaryote

2. Is the following sentence true or false? Plants make their own food in the process of photosynthesis. _____

3. Plant cells are enclosed by a _____.

4. Label the diagram of the plant cell below.

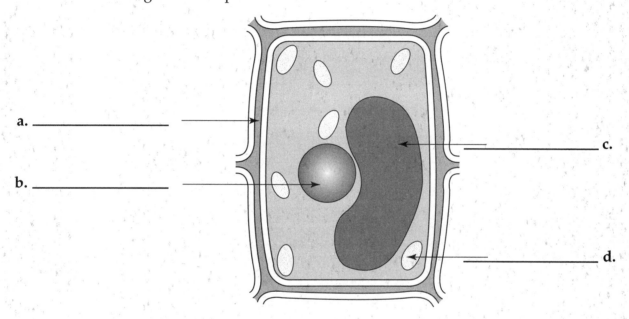

a. _____

b. _____

c.

d.

5. Is the following sentence true or false? Only some plants are multicellular. _____

6. Plants have levels of organization for _____ and _____.

7. The organ system that is above ground is the _____.

8. Below ground is the _____ system, which absorbs water and nutrients and anchors the plant in the soil.

The Plant Kingdom (continued)

Adaptations for Living on Land (pp. 354–355)

9. List five things that plants must do to survive on land.

    a. _____

    b._____

    c. _____

    d._____

    e. _____

10. Plants living on land get water and nutrients from the
    _____.

11. Why can a plant on land lose water and dry out?

    _____

    _____

    _____

    _____

12. Circle the letter of one adaptation that land plants have to keep from drying out.

    a. chlorophyll   **b.** cell wall

    c. cuticle   **d.** zygote

13. Some plants move water, minerals, and food with a system of tubelike structures called _____.

14. Is the following sentence true or false? Some land plants are supported by rigid cell walls and vascular tissue. _____

Structure and Function of Plants • *Reading/Notetaking Guide*

15. What occurs during fertilization?

_____

_____

16. Circle the letter of the name of a fertilized egg.
   a. sporophyte
   b. gamete
   c. gametophyte
   d. zygote

17. Is the following sentence true or false? All plants need water in their environment to reproduce. _____

Classification of Plants (pp. 356–358)

18. Is the following sentence true or false? Nonvascular plants can grow very tall. _____

19. Why are vascular plants better suited to life in dry areas?

_____

_____

20. How do biologists learn which organisms were the ancestors of today's plants?

_____

_____

21. Why do biologists think that ancient green algae were the ancestors of today's plants?

_____

_____

Complex Life Cycles (pp. 358–359)

22. Plants produce spores during the _____ stage and produce sex cells during the _____ stage.

23. Is the following sentence true or false? The sporophyte of a plant looks the same as the gametophyte. _____

24. What are two kinds of sex cells that a gametophyte produces?

   a. _____ **b.** _____

Plants Without Seeds

Key Concepts

■ What characteristics do the three groups of nonvascular plants share?

■ What characteristics do the three groups of seedless vascular plants share?

There are three major groups of nonvascular plants: mosses, liverworts, and hornworts. These low-growing plants live in moist areas where they can absorb water and other nutrients directly from their environment. The watery surroundings also enable sperm cells to swim to egg cells during reproduction.

The familiar green, fuzzy part of the moss is the gametophyte generation of the plant. Structures that look like tiny leaves grow off a small, stemlike structure. Thin, rootlike structures called **rhizoids** anchor the moss and absorb water and nutrients. The sporophyte generation grows out of the gametophyte. The sporophyte includes a long, slender stalk with a capsule at the end. The capsule contains spores.

Liverworts are often found growing as a thick crust on moist rocks or soil along the sides of a stream. Hornworts grow hornlike structures that are the sporophytes. Hornworts usually live in moist soil, often mixed in with grass plants.

Ferns, horsetails, and club mosses have true vascular tissue, and they do not produce seeds. Instead of seeds, these plants reproduce by releasing spores. Seedless vascular plants have true stems, roots, and leaves.

Vascular plants can grow quite tall because their vascular tissue provides an effective way of transporting materials throughout the plant. Vascular tissue also gives the plants strength and stability.

Seedless vascular plants need to grow in moist surroundings because they produce spores. These spores grow into gametophytes. When the gametophytes produce egg cells and sperm cells, there must be enough water available for fertilization.

Most ferns have underground stems. Leaves grow upward from the top side of the stems, while roots grow downward from the bottom of the stems. The roots anchor the fern to the ground and absorb water and nutrients from the soil. The leaves of ferns are called **fronds.** The upper surface of each frond is coated with a cuticle that helps the plant retain water. The familiar fern, with its visible fronds, is the sporophyte stage of the plant. Spores develop in tiny spore cases on the underside of the mature fronds. The spores develop into tiny gametophytes that grow low to the ground.

Two other groups of seedless vascular plants are the horsetails and club mosses. There are relatively few species of horsetails and club mosses alive today.

Structure and Function of Plants • *Reading/Notetaking Guide*

Plants Without Seeds (pp. 360–364)

This section describes the characteristics of nonvascular plants and seedless vascular plants.

Use Target Reading Skills

As you read the section, write the main idea—the biggest or most important idea—in the graphic organizer below. Then write three supporting details that give examples of the main idea.

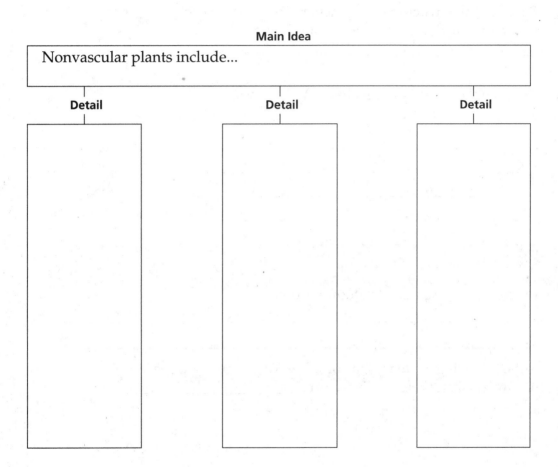

Main Idea

Nonvascular plants include...

Detail

Detail

Detail

Nonvascular Plants (pp. 360–361)

1. List two characteristics of nonvascular plants.

    a. _____

    b. _____

2. Is the following sentence true or false? Nonvascular plants can become very large and tall because of their support system. _____

Structure and Function of Plants • *Reading/Notetaking Guide*

Plants Without Seeds *(continued)*

3. How do nonvascular plants get water and other nutrients?

_____

_____

4. Is the following true or false? Nonvascular plants must have water to let the sperm cells swim to the egg cells. _____

5. Label and circle the gametophyte and the sporophyte in the diagram of the moss.

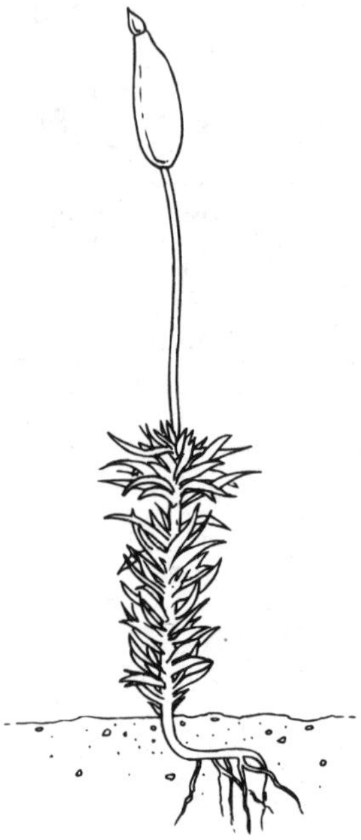

6. Thin, rootlike structures that anchor moss and absorb water and nutrients from the soil are called

_____.

7. Describe the sporophyte generation of a moss.

_____

_____

_____

_____

_____

_____

8. Where are liverworts often found growing?

_____

_____

9. Is the following sentence true or false? There are more species of hornworts than there are liverworts. _____

Structure and Function of Plants • *Reading/Notetaking Guide*

Seedless Vascular Plants (pp. 362–364)

10. List two characteristics that ferns, club mosses, and horsetails share.

    a. _____

    b. _____

11. Circle the letter of each sentence that is true about vascular tissue.

    a. Plants can grow tall without vascular tissue.
    b. Nonvascular plants are better suited to life on land.
    c. Vascular tissue transports water and food throughout a plant's body.
    d. Vascular tissue gives a plant strength and stability.

12. Why must ferns, club mosses, and horsetails grow in moist surroundings?

    _____

    _____

    _____

13. Is the following sentence true or false? Ferns are small plants that can only grow low to the ground. _____

14. Fern leaves are called _____.

15. What is the function of the cuticle on the upper surface of fern leaves?

    _____

16. Where do spores develop on a fern?

    _____

17. How are club mosses and horsetails similar to ferns?

    _____

    _____

    _____

18. Circle the letter before each sentence that is true about club mosses and horsetails.

    a. There are thousands of different species of club mosses and horsetails.
    b. Club mosses usually grow in moist woodlands and near streams.
    c. Club mosses have jointed stems with long, needlelike branches that grow in a circle around each joint.
    d. Horsetail stems contain silica, a gritty substance also found in sand.

The Characteristics of Seed Plants

Key Concepts

- What characteristics do seed plants share?
- How do seeds become new plants?

Seed plants share two important characteristics. They have vascular tissue, and they use pollen and seeds to reproduce. They all have body plans that include leaves, stems, and roots. Like seedless plants, seed plants have complex life cycles that include the sporophyte and gametophyte stages. In seed plants, the plants you see are the sporophytes. The gametophytes are microscopic.

Water, food, and minerals are transported throughout plants in vascular tissue. There are two types of vascular tissue. **Phloem** is the vascular tissue through which food moves. When food is made in the plant's leaves, it enters the phloem and travels to other parts of the plant. Water and minerals travel in the vascular tissue called **xylem.** The plant's roots absorb water and minerals from the soil. These materials enter the root's xylem and move upward into the stems and leaves.

Seed plants can live in a variety of environments. They produce **pollen,** tiny structures that contain the cells that later become sperm cells. Pollen delivers sperm cells directly near the eggs; therefore, seed plants do not need water for fertilization to occur. A **seed** is a structure that contains a young plant inside a protective covering. **Inside a seed is a partially developed plant. If a seed lands in an area where conditions are favorable, the plant sprouts out of the seed and begins to grow.** A seed has three main parts— an embryo, stored food, and a seed coat.

The young plant that develops from the zygote, or fertilized egg, is called the **embryo** and has the beginnings of roots, stems, and leaves. The embryo also has one or two seed leaves, or **cotyledons.** In some seeds, the cotyledons store food. The outer covering of a seed is called the seed coat. A seed may remain inactive for awhile. After seeds have formed, they are dispersed, sometimes far from where they were produced. Seeds are dispersed in many ways. One method involves organisms. Animals eat fruits, and the seeds pass through their digestive system and are deposited in new areas. Other seeds attach to an animal's fur or people's clothes. A second means of dispersal is water. A third method involves wind. Finally, some plants eject their seeds in a way that scatters the seeds in many directions.

Germination occurs when the embryo begins to grow again and pushes out of the seed. The embryo uses its stored food to begin to grow. First its roots grow downward, and then its stem and leaves grow upward. The temperature and moisture must be just right in order for a seed to germinate. A seed that is dispersed far from its parent plant has a better chance of survival.

The Characteristics of Seed Plants (pp. 365–369)

This section tells about the characteristics of seed plants and how seeds become new plants.

Use Target Reading Skills

As you read, make an outline about seed plants that you can use for review. Use the red headings for the main topics and blue headings for the supporting ideas.

The Characteristics of Seed Plants
I. What is a Seed Plant?
A. Vascular Tissue
B.
II. How Seeds Become New Plants
A.
B.
C.

What Is a Seed Plant? (pp. 365–366)

1. Circle the letter of each sentence that is true about seed plants.

   a. Seedless plants outnumber seed plants.
   b. Seed plants do not have vascular tissue.
   c. Seed plants use seeds to reproduce.
   d. All seed plants have roots, leaves, and stems.

2. In seed plants, the plants that you see are in the _____ stage of the life cycle. The _____ stage is microscopic.

3. In what two ways does vascular tissue help seed plants to live on land?

   a. _____

   b. _____

   _____

4. Circle the letter of the vascular tissue through which food moves.

   a. xylem
   b. phloem
   c. roots
   d. stems

Structure and Function of Plants ▪ *Reading/Notetaking Guide*

The Characteristics of Seed Plants *(continued)*

5. Circle the letter of the vascular tissue through which water moves.

   a. xylem
   b. phloem
   c. roots
   d. stems

6. Food made in the plant's _____ travels to the roots and stems.

7. Water and nutrients absorbed by the plant's _____ travel to the stems and leaves.

8. What is a seed?

   _____

   _____

9. Is the following sentence true or false? Pollen delivers sperm cells directly near the eggs. _____

How Seeds Become New Plants (pp. 367–369)

Match the part of the seed with its function.

Seed Part	Function
____ **10.** embryo	**a.** Keeps the seed from drying out
____ **11.** cotyledon	**b.** Young plant that develops from the fertilized egg
____ **12.** seed coat	**c.** A seed leaf that sometimes stores food

13. What do seeds need to develop into a new plant?

    _____

    _____

14. Is the following sentence true or false? Seeds can begin to grow in any place they land. _____

Structure and Function of Plants • *Reading/Notetaking Guide*

15. Complete the concept map to show ways that seeds are dispersed.

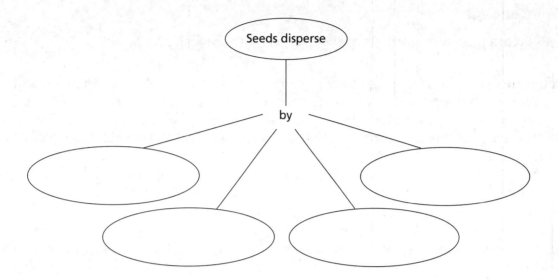

16. What is germination?

_____

_____

17. Circle the letter of each sentence that is true about germination.

    a. All seeds germinate immediately after they are dispersed.

    b. The embryo uses its stored food to begin to grow.

    c. First, the embryo's leaves and stem grow upward.

    d. Seeds that are dispersed far away from the parent have a better chance of survival.

Chapter 10 Structure and Function of Plants • *Section 4 Summary*

Roots, Stems, and Leaves

Key Concept

■ What are the main functions of roots, stems, and leaves?

Roots anchor a plant in the ground, absorb water and minerals from the soil, and sometimes store food. The two main types of root systems are fibrous root systems and taproot systems. A fibrous root system consists of many similarly sized roots that form a dense, tangled mass. A taproot system has one long, thick main root. Many smaller roots branch off the main root.

The tip of the root is rounded and covered by a **root cap.** The root cap protects the root from injury by rocks as the root grows through the soil. Root hairs grow out of the root's surface. These tiny hairs can enter the spaces between soil particles, where they absorb water and minerals. Root hairs help the plant absorb large amounts of substances. The root hairs also help to anchor the plant in the soil. Water and nutrients quickly move into the xylem, where they are transported upward to the plant's stem and leaves. Phloem transports food manufactured in the leaves to the root.

The stem produces branches, leaves, and flowers. It carries substances between the plant's roots and leaves. The stem also provides support for the plant and holds up the leaves so they are exposed to the sun. Some stems store food. Stems consist of vascular tissue and many supporting cells. Bundles of xylem and phloem run all the way up from the roots to the leaves. Buds are found where the leaves meet the stem. They contain tissue that can differentiate into new branches and leaves.

Stems can be herbaceous or woody. Herbaceous stems contain no wood and are often soft. Woody stems contain several layers of tissue. The outermost layer is bark, which includes an outer protective layer and an inner layer of living phloem to transport food through the stem. Next is a layer of cells called the **cambium.** These cells divide to produce new phloem and xylem. Annual rings are made of xylem. One pair of light and dark rings represents one year's growth. You can estimate a tree's age by counting its annual rings. The width of a tree's annual rings can also provide clues about past weather conditions.

The structure of leaves is adapted for capturing the sun's energy and carrying out photosynthesis. The leaf's top and bottom surface layers protect the cells inside. The surface layers have stomata, which are pores that open and close to control when gases enter and leave the leaf. The cells that contain the most chloroplasts are located near the leaf's upper surface, where they get the most light. Chlorophyll in the chloroplasts traps the sun's energy.

Carbon dioxide enters the leaf through open stomata. During photosynthesis, sugar and oxygen are produced from carbon dioxide and water. Oxygen passes out of the leaf through the open stomata. The sugar enters the phloem and then travels throughout the plant.

The process by which water evaporates from a plant's leaves is called **transpiration.** Without a way to slow down the process of transpiration, a plant would shrivel up and die. One way that plants retain water is by closing their stomata. The stomata often close when a plant's leaves start to dry out.

Structure and Function of Plants · *Reading/Notetaking Guide*

Roots, Stems, and Leaves (pp. 370–375)

This section explains the main functions of roots, stems, and leaves.

Use Target Reading Skills

Before you read, use the headings to ask questions about the material. As you read, write the answers to the questions.

The Structure and Function of Seed Plants

Question	Answer
What are the main functions of roots?	

Roots (pp. 370–371)

1. List three functions of roots.

    a. _____

    b. _____

    c. _____

2. Look at the two types of root systems illustrated below. Label the roots as taproot or fibrous roots.

a. _____   b. _____

Structure and Function of Plants • *Reading/Notetaking Guide*

Roots, Stems, and Leaves (continued)

Match the root structure with its function.

Root Structure	Function
_____ 3. root cap	a. Moves food to the roots and other parts of plant
_____ 4. root hairs	b. Protects the root from injury during growth
_____ 5. phloem	c. Moves water and minerals to the stems and leaves
_____ 6. xylem	d. Increase the amount of water and minerals absorbed by the root

Stems (pp. 372–373)

7. List three functions of stems.

   a. _____

   b. _____

   c. _____

8. What is the structure of a stem?

   _____

   _____

   _____

9. List the two types of stems.

   a. _____

   b. _____

10. Is the following sentence true or false? Herbaceous stems are hard and rigid and have an outer layer called bark. _____

11. What is heartwood?

    _____

    _____

12. What is cambium?

    _____

    _____

13. Circle the letter before the tissue that makes up a tree's annual rings.

    a. xylem   b. phloem
    c. cambium   d. bark

14. Is the following sentence true or false? One year's growth of a tree is represented by one pair of light and dark rings in the tree's stem. _____

Structure and Function of Plants • *Reading/Notetaking Guide*

15. What information do annual rings provide about a tree?

_____

Leaves (pp. 374–375)

16. What role do leaves play in a plant?

_____

_____

_____

Match the leaf part with its function.

Leaf Part	Function
____ **17.** cuticle	**a.** Widely spaced cells allow carbon dioxide and oxygen to pass in and out of the leaf.
____ **18.** xylem	
____ **19.** phloem	**b.** Carries water from the roots to the leaves
____ **20.** stomata	**c.** Waxy, waterproof coating that covers a leaf's surface
____ **21.** lower leaf cells	**d.** Contain the most chloroplasts
____ **22.** upper leaf cells	**e.** Carries food made in the leaves to the rest of the plant
	f. Tiny pores that open and close to let carbon dioxide in and water vapor and oxygen out

23. Is the following sentence true or false? The upper leaf cells are tightly packed to trap the energy in sunlight. _____

24. Photosynthesis can be summarized by this equation:

$$\text{water } + \underline{\hspace{2cm}} \xrightarrow{\text{light energy}} \underline{\hspace{2cm}} + \underline{\hspace{2cm}}$$

25. The process by which water evaporates from a plant's leaves is called

_____.

26. Is the following sentence true or false? Stomata close to keep the plant from losing water. _____

Reproduction in Seed Plants

Key Concepts

- What are the characteristics of gymnosperms and how do they reproduce?
- What are the characteristics of angiosperms and their flowers?
- How do angiosperms reproduce?
- What are the two types of angiosperms?

A **gymnosperm** is a seed plant that produces naked seeds—seeds that are not enclosed by a protective fruit. **Every gymnosperm produces naked seeds. In addition, many gymnosperms have needle-like or scalelike leaves and deep-growing root systems.** Gymnosperms are classified into cycads, conifers, ginkgoes, and gnetophytes.

Most gymnosperms have reproductive structures called **cones**. Male cones produce pollen. Female cones contain at least one ovule. An **ovule** is a structure that contains an egg cell. After being fertilized, the ovule develops into a seed. To reproduce, **first, pollen falls from a male cone onto a female cone. In time, a sperm cell and an egg cell join together in an ovule on the female cone.** The transfer of pollen from a male reproductive structure to a female reproductive structure is called **pollination.**

Angiosperms are a group of seed plants. **All angiosperms, or flowering plants, share two important traits. First, they produce flowers. Second, in contrast to gymnosperms, which produce uncovered seeds, angiosperms produce seeds that are enclosed in fruits.**

Flowers come in all sorts of shapes, sizes, and colors. But, despite their differences, all flowers have the same function—reproduction. A **flower** is the reproductive structure of an angiosperm. A flower bud is enclosed by leaflike structures called **sepals** that protect the developing flower. Most flowers have **petals**—colorful, leaflike structures. Within the petals are the flower's reproductive parts. Thin stalks topped by small knobs inside the flower are **stamens,** the male reproductive parts. A stamen consists of an anther and a filament. Pollen is produced in the anther. The female part, or **pistil,** consists of a stigma, style, and ovary. An **ovary** is a flower structure that protects seeds as they develop. An ovary contains one or more ovules. For angiosperms to reproduce, **first, pollen falls on a flower's stigma. In time, the sperm cell and egg cell join together in the flower's ovule. The zygote develops into the embryo part of the seed.** As the seed develops after fertilization, the ovary eventually becomes a **fruit**—a ripened ovary and other structures that enclose one or more seeds.

Angiosperms are divided into two major groups: monocots and dicots. Monocots are angiosperms that have only one seed leaf. **Dicots** produce seeds with two seed leaves.

Seed plants have many uses. For example, paper, lumber, turpentine, and other products come from gymnosperms. Angiosperms provide food and are used to make clothing, rubber, and furntiure.

Structure and Function of Plants • *Reading/Notetaking Guide*

Reproduction in Seed Plants (pp. 378–387)

This section gives examples of the group of seed plants known as gymnosperms and angiosperms and describes their features and how they reproduce.

Use Target Reading Skills

After reading the section, complete the two cycle diagrams. One represents the life cycle of gymnosperms, and the other represents the life cycle of angiosperms.

Life Cycle of a Gymnosperm

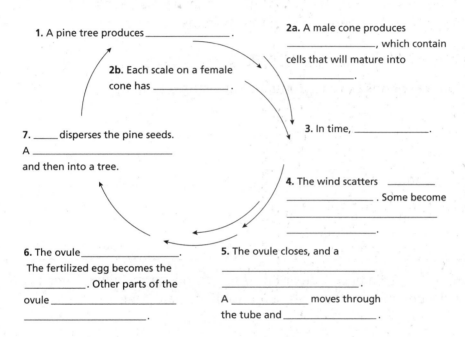

Life Cycle of an Angiosperm

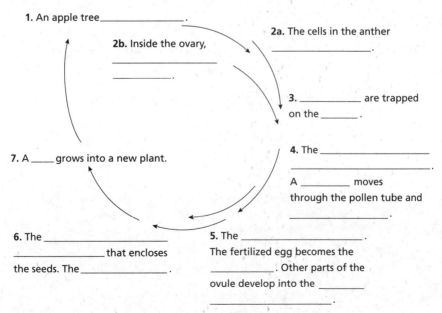

Structure and Function of Plants • *Reading/Notetaking Guide*

Reproduction in Seed Plants *(continued)*

Gymnosperms (pp. 378–379)

1. What is a gymnosperm?

   _____

   _____

2. Is the following sentence true or false? Gymnosperms have seeds that are not enclosed by a fruit. _____

3. Is the following sentence true or false? Gymnosperms have needle-like or scalelike leaves and deep-growing root systems. _____

Gymnosperm Life Cycle (pp. 380–381)

4. Most gymnosperms have reproductive structures called

   _____.

5. Is the following sentence true or false? Male cones contain ovules at the base of each scale. _____

6. A structure that contains an egg cell is a(n) _____.

7. What happens during pollination?

   _____

   _____

8. Is the following sentence true or false? In gymnosperms, wind often carries the pollen from the male cones to the female cones.

   _____

9. It can take up to _____ for the seeds of some gynosperms to mature. During that time, the female cone _____.

Angiosperms (p. 382)

10. A plant that produces seeds that are enclosed in a fruit is called a(n)

    _____.

11. List two characteristics of angiosperms.

    a. _____

    b. _____

Structure and Function of Plants ▪ *Reading/Notetaking Guide*

The Structure of Flowers (pp. 382–383)

12. Label the parts of the flower in this diagram.

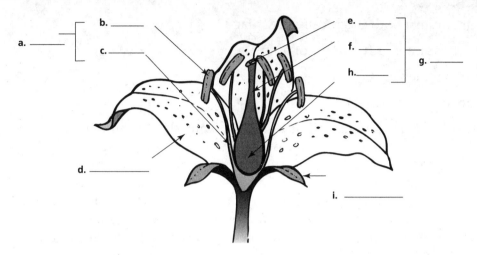

13. What are pollinators?

_____

Angiosperm Life Cycle (pp. 384–385)

14. Is the following sentence true or false? All angiosperms rely on wind for pollination. _____

15. Describe the fertilization process.

_____

_____

_____

Types of Angiosperms (p. 386)

16. List the two major groups of angiosperms.

a. _____   b. _____

17. What are three ways in which monocots and dicots differ?

_____

_____

_____

Seed Plants in Everyday Life (p. 387)

18. Circle the letter of each product that conifers provide.

      a. fruit   **b.** paper   **c.** turpentine   **d.** cotton fibers

19. Is the following sentence true or false? Angiosperms are an important source of food for other organisms. _____

What Is an Animal?

Key Concepts

- How are animal bodies typically organized?
- What are four major functions of animals?
- What is symmetry?
- How are animals classified?

An organism's structure is called its **anatomy**. Animals are composed of many cells, the basic units that carry out life functions. **Physiology** is the study of functions in organisms. **The cells of most animals are organized into higher levels of structure, including tissues, organs, and systems.** A tissue is a group of similar cells that perform a specific function. Tissues may combine to form an organ. An organ is a group of different tissues that performs a more complex function than each tissue could perform alone. In most animals, organs combine to form organ systems.

Some major functions of animals are obtaining food and oxygen, keeping internal conditions stable, moving, and reproducing. Structures or behaviors that allow animals to perform these basic functions in their environments are called adaptations.

Animals obtain food by eating other organisms. The body's cells need oxygen to release energy from food. All animals move at some point in their lives. Most animals produce offspring by sexual reproduction, the process by which a new organism develops from the joining of two sex cells. The joining of an egg cell and a sperm cell is called fertilization. Some animals reproduce by asexual reproduction, in which an organism produces an identical copy of itself.

The functions an animal carries out are closely related to its body structure. **Symmetry is a balanced arrangement of body parts that is characteristic of many animals.** An animal has **bilateral symmetry** if there is just one line that divides it into halves that are mirror images. An animal with **radial symmetry** has many lines of symmetry that divide it into two symmetrical halves. Some animals have no symmetry. Animals with radial symmetry do not have distinct front or back ends. All animals with radial symmetry live in the water. Animals with bilateral symmetry are usually larger and more complex. They have sense organs in their front ends that pick up information about what is in front of them.

Biologists have defined 35 major groups of animals, each of which is called a **phylum** (plural: *phyla*). Biologists hypothesize that all animals arose from single-celled organisms. **Animals are classified according to how they are related to other animals. These relationships are determined by the animal's body structure, the way the animal develops, and its DNA.** One important structural characteristic used to classify animals is whether or not the animal has a backbone. Animals without backbones make up most of the animal species on Earth. These animals are called **invertebrates.** Animals with backbones are called **vertebrates.**

Structure and Function of Invertebrates • *Reading/Notetaking Guide*

What Is an Animal? (pp. 410–416)

This section explains the basic characteristics and major functions of animals. It also describes how biologists classify animals into groups and presents the different types of symmetry.

Use Target Reading Skills

As you read, take notes on the main ideas in the section and the important details that support each main idea. Think about the Key Concepts and Key Terms. Use the graphic organizer below to help you take notes.

What Is an Animal?

Recall Clues and Questions	Notes
What is a cell?	A cell is …

Structure of Animals (p. 411)

1. What are cells?

_____

_____

Structure and Function of Invertebrates ▪ *Reading/Notetaking Guide*

What Is an Animal? *(continued)*

2. List the three levels of organization in animals and the structure and function of each level.

    a. _____

    b. _____

    c. _____

Functions of Animals (pp. 412–413)

3. What are four major functions of animals?

    a. _____

    b. _____

    c. _____

    d. _____

4. What is an adaptation?

    _____

    _____

    _____

Structure and Function of Invertebrates • *Reading/Notetaking Guide*

Match the needs with how animals use them.

Use in Animals	Needs

_____ 5. Gives animals raw
materials for growth and
energy

_____ 6. Needed by body cells to
release the energy from
food

a. oxygen

b. food

7. Is the following sentence true or false? Most animals have a cavity inside
their body where food is broken down into substances the body can use.

_____

8. Why must animals maintain a stable environment within their bodies?

_____

_____

9. What are most animal movements related to?

a. _____

b. _____

10. Is the following sentence true or false? Some animals don't move from
place to place. _____

11. What is sexual reproduction?

_____

_____

_____

12. The joining of an egg cell and a sperm cell is called _____.

13. What is asexual reproduction?

_____

_____

_____

14. Is the following sentence true or false? Asexual reproduction involves
the joining of sex cells from two parents. _____

Structure and Function of Invertebrates • *Reading/Notetaking Guide*

What Is an Animal? *(continued)*

Symmetry (p. 414)

15. The balanced arrangement of an animal's body is called

    _____.

16. Because a butterfly can be divided into two halves that are mirror images, it has _____ symmetry.

17. Animals with many lines of symmetry that all go through a central point have _____ symmetry.

18. Is the following sentence true or false? Some animals have no symmetry.

    _____

19. Circle the letter of each sentence that is true about bilateral symmetry.
    a. Human bodies have bilateral symmetry.
    b. Animals with radial symmetry are usually larger and more complex than animals with bilateral symmetry.
    c. Bilateral symmetry allows for a streamlined, balanced body that moves quickly and efficiently.
    d. Most animals with bilateral symmetry have sense organs in their back ends.

Classification of Animals (pp. 415–416)

20. Biologists classify animals in the animal kingdom into about 35 major groups, each of which is called a(n) _____.

21. Look at the branching tree of animal phyla in your textbook. Circle the letter of the animal group that is most closely related to birds.
    a. insects
    b. mammals
    c. amphibians
    d. reptiles

Structure and Function of Invertebrates • *Reading/Notetaking Guide*

22. Is the following sentence true or false? Evidence suggests that all animals arose from single-celled ancestors. _____

23. What do biologists consider when they classify an animal?

    a. _____

    b. _____

    c. _____

24. Is the following sentence true or false? An animal that does not have a backbone is called a vertebrate. _____

Chapter 11 Structure and Function of Invertebrates ▪ *Section 2 Summary*

Sponges and Cnidarians

Key Concepts
- What are the main characteristics of sponges?
- What are the main characteristics of cnidarians?

Sponges and cnidarians are animals that live in water. **Sponges are invertebrate animals that usually have no body symmetry and never have tissues or organs.** Sponges stay in one place, attached to hard surfaces. Structures surrounding the central cavity of a sponge are adapted for different functions. Water enters through pores and carries food and oxygen into the sponge. Water also carries the sponge's waste products away.

Sponges reproduce both asexually and sexually. In sexual reproduction, water currents carry sperm from one sponge into the pores of another sponge. These sperm fertilize the sponge's egg cells. After fertilization, a **larva** develops. A larva is an immature form of an animal that looks very different from the adult.

Jellyfishes, sea anemones, and corals are **cnidarians,** invertebrates that have stinging cells and take food into a central body cavity. **Cnidarians use stinging cells to capture food and defend themselves.**

There are two cnidarian body plans, **polyp** and **medusa.** A polyp, such as a sea anemone, is shaped something like a vase, with the mouth opening at the top. In contrast, a medusa, such as a jellyfish, is shaped like a bowl, with a mouth that opens downward. A medusa, unlike a polyp, is adapted for a swimming life. Some cnidarians are polyps at one point in their lives and medusas at another point. Other cnidarians are either a polyp or a medusa for all their lives.

A cnidarian captures its food by using its stinging cells. The stinging cells release a spined structure that snares the prey. Some stinging cells also release venom.

Cnidarians reproduce both asexually and sexually. For polyps such as hydras, corals, and sea anemones, budding is the most common form of asexual reproduction. In budding, small new animals grow from the side of an adult animal. Sexual reproduction occurs in a variety of ways. Some species of cnidarians have both sexes within one individual. In others, the sexes are separate individuals. Many cnidarians have a life cycle, or a sequence of different stages of development.

Structure and Function of Invertebrates • *Reading/Notetaking Guide*

Sponges and Cnidarians (pp. 417–421)

This section describes the characteristics of sponges and cnidarians.

Use Target Reading Skills

As you read, take notes on the main ideas in the section and the important details that support each main idea. Think about the Key Concepts and Key Terms. Use the graphic organizer below to help you take notes.

Sponges and Cnidarians

Recall Clues and Questions	Notes
What is a sponge?	A sponge is . . .

Sponges (pp. 303–305)

1. Describe the body of a sponge.

   _____

   _____

2. Circle the letter of each sentence that is true about sponges.

   a. Sponges usually have no body symmetry.
   b. Sponges always have tissues and organs.
   c. A sponge gets oxygen from water.
   d. Adult sponges do not to attach themselves to
       hard surfaces underwater.

Structure and Function of Invertebrates ▪ *Reading/Notetaking Guide*

Sponges and Cnidarians *(continued)*

3. A network of _____ supports the bodies of most sponges.

4. How do sponges reproduce sexually?

   _____

   _____

5. After fertilization, a _____ , or an immature form of the animal, develops.

Cnidarians *(pp. 419–421)*

6. What are cnidarians?

   _____

   _____

7. Circle the letter of each characteristic of a polyp.

   a. mouth opens at top
   b. attached to underwater surface
   c. shaped like upside-down bowl
   d. tentacles spread out from around the mouth

8. In this diagram, identify which body form is a polyp and which is a medusa. Then label the mouth and central cavity for each.

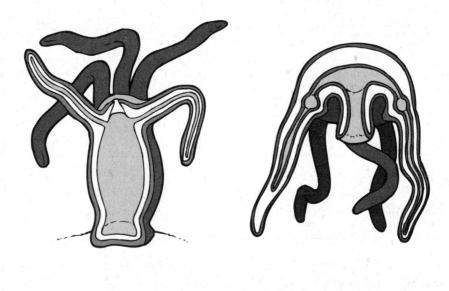

   _____   _____

Structure and Function of Invertebrates • *Reading/Notetaking Guide*

9. How does a cnidarian capture prey?

_____

_____

_____

10. Is the following sentence true or false? A jellyfish is not able to swim.

_____

11. Circle the letter of each sentence that is true about cnidarians.

    a. Cnidarians use stinging cells to capture prey.

    b. Cnidarians take food into a central body cavity.

    c. Cnidarians expel undigested food through the mouth.

    d. Cnidarians cannot move.

12. How do cnidarians reproduce?

_____

_____

_____

Worms and Mollusks

Key Concepts

■ What are the main characteristics of worms?

■ What are the main characteristics of each phylum of worms?

■ What are the main characteristics of mollusks?

■ What are the main groups of mollusks?

All worms are invertebrates that have long, narrow bodies without legs. Biologists classify worms into three major phyla—flatworms, roundworms, and segmented worms. Worms have bilateral symmetry. They have tissues, organs, and body systems. They reproduce both sexually and asexually.

Flatworms include planarians, flukes, and tapeworms. **Flatworms are flat and as soft as jelly.** Many flatworms are parasites. A **parasite** is an organism that lives inside or on another organism. The parasite takes its food from its **host,** the organism in or on which it lives. A tapeworm is a kind of parasitic flatworm.

Roundworms have cylindrical bodies. **Unlike cnidarians or flatworms, roundworms have a digestive system that is like a tube, open at both ends.** Food enters through the mouth. Wastes leave the digestive system through the **anus,** an opening at the other end of the tube.

Earthworms and other segmented worms have bodies made up of many linked sections called segments. Segmented worms have a **closed circulatory system.** In a closed system, such as your own, the blood flows only through connected tubes called blood vessels.

Mollusks are invertebrates with soft, unsegmented bodies that are often protected by a hard outer shell. **In addition to a soft body often covered by a shell, a mollusk has a thin layer of tissue called a mantle that covers its internal organs, and an organ called a foot.** Mollusks have bilateral symmetry and a digestive system with two openings.

Most species of mollusks have an **open circulatory system,** in which the blood is not always inside blood vessels. Most mollusks that live in water have **gills,** organs that allow oxygen from the water to enter the body.

Biologists classify mollusks into groups based on physical characteristics. **The three major groups of mollusks are gastropods, bivalves, and cephalopods.**

Gastropods are the largest group of mollusks, and include snails and slugs. Gastropods have a single external shell or no shell at all.

Clams, oysters, scallops, and mussels are bivalves. Bivalves are mollusks that have two shells held together by hinges and strong muscles.

Octopuses, cuttlefish, nautiluses, and squids are **cephalopods.** A cephalopod is an ocean-dwelling mollusk whose foot is adapted to form tentacles around its mouth. Cephalopods are carnivores.

Structure and Function of Invertebrates • *Reading/Notetaking Guide*

Worms and Mollusks (pp. 424–432)

This section tells about the characteristics of the three main groups of worms and the main characteristics of mollusks.

Use Target Reading Skills

As you read, take notes on the main ideas in the section and the important details that support each main idea. Think about the Key Concepts and Key Terms. Use the graphic organizer below to help you take notes.

Worms and Mollusks

Recall Clues and Questions	Notes
What are the characteristics of worms?	Worms are …

Characteristics of Worms (pp. 424–425)

1. What are the three major phyla of worms?

   _____

2. List five characteristics shared by all worms.

   a. _____

   b. _____

   c. _____

   d. _____

   e. _____

Worms and Mollusks *(continued)*

3. Circle the letter of each sentence that is true about worms.

   a. Worms do not have brains.

   b. A worm has sense organs in its head end to respond to food, mates, and predators.

   c. Worms can only reproduce sexually.

   d. In some worm species, each individual has both male and female sex organs.

Flatworms (pp. 426–427)

4. Circle the letter of each characteristic of most flatworms.

   a. flat bodies

   b. round bodies

   c. include tapeworms and planarians

   d. one-way digestive system

5. An organism that lives inside or on another organism and takes its food from that organism is a(n) _____.

6. Circle the letter of each characteristic of planarians.

   a. parasite

   b. scavenger

   c. herbivore

   d. predator

7. Describe how a planarian feeds.

   _____

   _____

   _____

8. Is the following sentence true or false? Planarians rely on their eyesight to find food. _____

9. What is a tapeworm?

   _____

   _____

Structure and Function of Invertebrates ▪ *Reading/Notetaking Guide*

Roundworms (p. 428)

10. Circle the letter of each sentence that is true about roundworms.

    a. Roundworms can live in nearly any dry environment.

    b. Roundworms have flat bodies.

    c. Most roundworms are tiny and hard to see.

    d. Roundworms have a digestive system that is like a tube, open at both ends.

11. Wastes exit a roundworm's digestive system through an opening called the _____.

12. What is the advantage of a one-way digestive system?

_____

_____

Segmented Worms (p. 429)

13. Circle the letter of each sentence that is true about segmented worms.

    a. Segmented worms have an open circulatory system.

    b. Earthworms are a type of segmented worm.

    c. Segmented worms have bodies made up of many linked sections.

    d. Reproductive organs are found in every segment of an earthworm.

14. Earthworms have a digestive system with _____ opening(s).

15. What is the advantage of a closed circulatory system?

_____

_____

_____

Structure and Function of Invertebrates • *Reading/Notetaking Guide*

Worms and Mollusks *(continued)*

Characteristics of Mollusks (p. 430)

16. Circle the letter of each characteristic of a mollusk.
    a. vertebrate
    b. invertebrate
    c. segmented body
    d. unsegmented body

17. Give the function of each of the following parts of a mollusk.

    hard outer shell: _____

    mantle: _____

    foot: _____

18. Is the following sentence true or false? Mollusks are found only in dry places on land. _____

19. What is an open circulatory system?

    _____

    _____

20. What are the functions of gills and cilia?

    _____

    _____

Diversity of Mollusks (pp. 431–432)

21. List the characteristics that biologists use to classify mollusks.

    a. _____

    b. _____

    c. _____

Structure and Function of Invertebrates · *Reading/Notetaking Guide*

22. Complete the concept map to show the three major groups of mollusks.

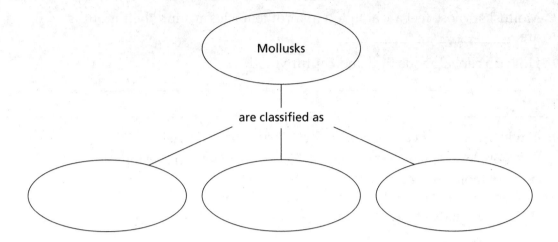

23. Mollusks that have a single shell or no shell at all are called
_____.

24. What is a radula? _____.

25. What are bivalves?

_____

_____

26. How are bivalves different from other mollusks?

_____

_____

_____

27. Circle the letter of each sentence that is true about bivalves.

    a. Bivalves use their gills to capture food.
    b. Bivalves live on land.
    c. Clams burrow in mud.
    d. A pearl forms in an oyster to protect the oyster from predators.

Structure and Function of Invertebrates ▪ *Reading/Notetaking Guide*

Worms and Mollusks *(continued)*

28. Mollusks whose feet are adapted to form tentacles around their mouths
are _____.

29. How do cephalopods find and capture food?

_____

_____

30. Circle the letter of each sentence that is true about cephalopods.

    a. Cephalopods have large eyes and a complex nervous system.

    b. Cephalopods cannot remember things.

    c. Cephalopods have closed circulatory systems.

    d. Cephalopods live in the ocean.

Arthropods

Key Concepts
- What are the general characteristics of arthropods?
- What are the distinguishing structures of insects, crustaceans, arachnids, and centipedes and millipedes?

The major groups of arthropods are crustaceans, arachnids, centipedes and millipedes, and insects. Arthropods are invertebrates that have an external skeleton, a segmented body, and jointed attachments called appendages. Arthropods have bilateral symmetry, an open circulatory system, a digestive system with two openings, and sexual reproduction.

All arthropods have a waxy **exoskeleton,** or outer skeleton, that protects the animal and helps prevent evaporation of water. Arthropods shed their outgrown exoskeletons in a process called **molting.** Arthropods have segmented bodies and jointed appendages that give them flexibility and enable them to move.

A crustacean is an arthropod that has two or three body sections, five or more pairs of legs, and two pairs of antennae. Crustaceans live in watery environments and must have gills. Most crustaceans begin their lives as microscopic, swimming larvae. Crustacean larvae develop into adults by **metamorphosis,** a process in which an animal's body undergoes dramatic changes in form.

Arachnids are arthropods with two body sections, four pairs of legs, and no antennae. The first body section is a combined head and midsection. The hind section, called the **abdomen,** contains the arachnid's reproductive organs and part of its digestive system. Spiders and ticks are arachnids.

Centipedes and millipedes are arthropods with two body sections and numerous pairs of legs. Centipedes have one pair of legs attached to each segment, and some centipedes have over 100 segments. Millipedes, which may have more than 80 segments, have two pairs of legs on each segment.

Insects are arthropods with three body sections, six legs, one pair of antennae, and usually one or two pairs of wings. The three body sections are the head, thorax, and abdomen. An insect's **thorax,** or midsection, is the section to which wings and legs are attached. The abdomen contains many of the insect's internal organs.

Insects begin life as tiny, hard-shelled, fertilized eggs. After they hatch, insects begin a process of metamorphosis that eventually produces an adult insect. **Each insect species undergoes either complete metamorphosis or gradual metamorphosis. Complete metamorphosis** has four stages: egg, larva, pupa, and adult. After a period of eating and growing, the larva goes into the next stage and becomes a **pupa** (plural: *pupae*). As a pupa, the insect is enclosed in a protective covering and gradually changes into an adult. In contrast, **gradual metamorphosis** has no distinct larval stage. An egg hatches into a **nymph** that often resembles the adult insect.

Structure and Function of Invertebrates • *Reading/Notetaking Guide*

Arthropods (pp. 434–441)

This section describes the characteristics of arthropods and the distinguishing structures of insects, crustaceans, arachnids, centipedes, and millipedes.

Use Target Reading Skills

As you read, take notes on the main ideas in the section and the important details that support each main idea. Think about the Key Concepts and Key Terms. Use the graphic organizer below to take notes.

Arthropods

Recall Clues and Questions	Notes
What is an arthropod?	An arthropod is . . .

Characteristics of Arthropods (pp. 435–436)

1. List four major groups of arthropods.

    a. _____ b. _____

    c. _____ d. _____

2. What are the characteristics of an arthropod?

    _____

    _____

    _____

3. Circle the letter of each example of an appendage found in arthropods.

    a. wings
    b. closed circulatory system
    c. digestive system with one opening
    d. legs

Structure and Function of Invertebrates · *Reading/Notetaking Guide*

4. How does an exoskeleton help arthropods live on land?

   _____

   _____

   _____

5. What happens to the exoskeleton when an arthropod grows?

   _____

   _____

   _____

6. Look at the table in your textbook comparing the largest arthropod groups. Crustaceans have _____ pairs of antennae. Arachnids have _____ body sections. Insects have _____ pairs of legs.

7. Is the following sentence true or false? Joints in their appendages give arthropods flexibility and the ability to move.

   _____

Match the type of appendage with its function.

Appendage	**Function**
_____ **8.** antennae	**a.** Walking, catching prey, defending against predators
_____ **9.** legs	**b.** Have sense organs for smelling, tasting, and touching

Structure and Function of Invertebrates ▪ *Reading/Notetaking Guide*

Arthropods *(continued)*

Diversity of Arthropods (pp. 436–438)

10. What is a crustacean?

_____

_____

_____

11. Circle the letter of each sentence that is true about crustaceans.

    a. Crustaceans get oxygen through gills.

    b. Crustaceans live only in dry areas on land.

    c. Most crustaceans begin their lives as tiny swimming larvae.

    d. Each body segment has one pair of legs attached to it.

12. Crustacean larvae develop into adults by _____,
a process in which an animal's body changes dramatically in a short time.

13. An arthropod with only two body sections and four pairs of legs is a(n)
_____.

14. Circle the letter of each characteristic of arachnids.

    a. Abdomen containing reproductive organs

    b. Four pairs of legs

    c. Four antennae

    d. Parasitic

15. Circle the letter of each sentence that is true about spiders.

    a. All spiders are herbivores.

    b. All spiders build webs to catch their prey.

    c. Spiders have hollow fangs that inject venom into prey.

    d. Spiders rarely bite people.

Structure and Function of Invertebrates ▪ *Reading/Notetaking Guide*

Match the arthropod with its characteristics. Each kind of arthropod may be used more than once.

Characteristics

____ **16.** Two pairs of legs on each segment

____ **17.** One pair of legs on each segment

____ **18.** Two body sections with one pair of antennae

____ **19.** Long abdomen with many segments

Arthropods

a. centipede

b. millipede

Structure and Function of Invertebrates • *Reading/Notetaking Guide*

Arthropods *(continued)*

Characteristics of Insects *(p. 439)*

20. What is an insect?

_____

_____

21. Circle the letter of the body section to which wings and legs are attached.

    a. head

    b. thorax

    c. abdomen

    d. exoskeleton

22. Identify the body sections of the grasshopper below.

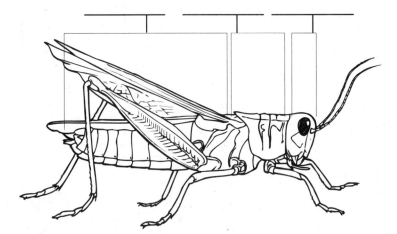

23. Each organ, tissue, and cell in an insect's nervous system contributes to the functions of _____ and _____.

Structure and Function of Invertebrates • *Reading/Notetaking Guide*

24. Insects have two _____ eyes, which contain many lenses.

25. Insects get oxygen into their bodies through a system of

_____.

26. Complete the cycle diagram to show the stages of complete metamorphosis.

Insect begins life as a tiny, hard-shelled,

fertilized _____ .

When its development is complete, the

_____ leaves the pupal

case. It feeds and finds mates.

Immature form of the insect that looks

very different from the adult is a(n)

_____ .

The insect is enclosed in a protective

covering. The insect at this stage is

called a(n) _____ .

27. In gradual metamorphosis, the egg hatches into a(n)
_____ , which looks much like a small adult.

Echinoderms

Key Concepts
- What are the main characteristics of echinoderms?
- What are the major groups of echinoderms?

Echinoderms are invertebrates with an internal skeleton and a system of fluid-filled tubes called a water vascular system. The skin of most echinoderms is stretched over an internal skeleton, called an **endoskeleton.** The **water vascular system** consists of fluid-filled tubes within the echinoderm's body. Portions of the tubes can squeeze together, forcing water into structures called **tube feet.** Most echinoderms use their tube feet to move and to capture food.

Almost all echinoderms are either male or female. Eggs are usually fertilized in the water. The fertilized eggs develop into larvae. The larvae eventually undergo metamorphosis and become adults.

There are four major groups of echinoderms: sea stars, brittle stars, sea urchins, and sea cucumbers. Sea stars are predators with five arms. A sea star uses its tube feet to move across the ocean bottom and capture prey. A sea star will grasp a clam with all five arms and pull the shells open. Then the sea star feeds on the clam's tissues.

Brittle stars have long and slender arms, with flexible joints. Brittle stars use their arms to slither along the ocean bottom. They use their tube feet to catch food.

Unlike sea stars and brittle stars, sea urchins have no arms. Movable spines cover and protect their bodies. Sea urchins move mostly by using bands of tube feet that extend out between the spines. They scrape and cut food with five teethlike structures.

Sea cucumbers move by using five rows of tube feet on their underside. Sea cucumbers use their tentacles to sweep food toward their mouths.

Structure and Function of Invertebrates • *Reading/Notetaking Guide*

Echinoderms (pp. 443–445)

This section explains the main characteristics of echinoderms.

Use Target Reading Skills

As you read, take notes on the main ideas in the section and the important details that support each main idea. Think about the Key Concepts and Key Terms. Use the graphic organizer below to help you take notes.

Echinoderms

Recall Clues and Questions	Notes
What are echinoderms?	Echinoderms are . . .

Characteristics of Echinoderms (pp. 443–444)

1. What is an echinoderm?

   _____

   _____

2. The skin of most echinoderms is stretched over an internal skeleton, called a(n) _____.

3. What is a water vascular system?

   _____

   _____

Structure and Function of Invertebrates • *Reading/Notetaking Guide*

Echinoderms *(continued)*

4. Label the parts of a sea star's water vascular system in the diagram below.

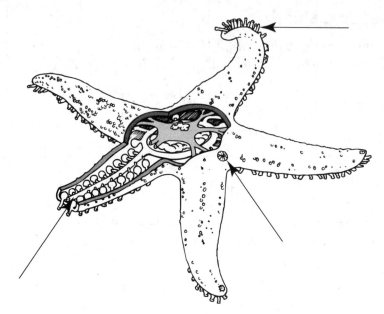

Diversity of Echinoderms (p. 445)

5. Is the following sentence true or false? A sea star will grasp a clam with all five arms, pull the shells open, and then feed on the clam's tissue.

   _____

6. Complete the table about the characteristics of other echinoderms.

Characteristics of Other Echinoderms			
Characteristics	**Brittle Stars**	**Sea Urchins**	**Sea Cucumbers**
How they get food			
Movement			

Name _____ Date _____ Class _____

What Is a Vertebrate?

Key Concepts
- What are the characteristics of chordates and vertebrates?

- How have scientists been able to infer the relationships of the major groups of vertebrates?

- How do vertebrates differ in the way they control body temperature?

Vertebrates are a subgroup of the phylum Chordata. All members of this phylum are called **chordates. At some point in their lives, all chordates have three characteristics: a notochord, a nerve cord that runs down their back, and slits in their throat area.** The **notochord** is a flexible rod that supports the chordate's back. In vertebrates, part or all of the notochord is replaced by a backbone. The nerve cord is the connection between the brain and the nerves. The slits in the throat area, called pharyngeal slits, disappear before birth in many vertebrates.

A vertebrate has a backbone that is part of an internal skeleton. The backbone is formed by many similar bones called **vertebrae** (singular *vertebra*). Each vertebra has a hole in it that allows the spinal cord to pass through it. The internal skeleton, or endoskeleton, supports and protects the body, helps give the body shape, and gives muscles a place to attach. In addition to the backbone, the vertebrate's endoskeleton includes the skull, ribs, and in many cases, arm and leg bones. The skull protects the brain and sense organs. The ribs protect the heart and lungs and other internal organs.

Vertebrates probably evolved from an invertebrate chordate ancestor. **By studying fossils and other evidence, such as DNA, scientists have been able to infer the relationships of the major groups of vertebrates—fishes, amphibians, reptiles, birds, and mammals.** Fossils show that the first vertebrates were probably fishes, which appeared on Earth more than 500 million years ago. Amphibians descended from fishes. Then, amphibians gave rise to reptiles. Both mammals and birds descended from reptiles. Birds were the latest group of vertebrates to arise.

One characteristic that differs among the major groups of vertebrates is the way they control their body temperature. **The body temperature of most fishes, amphibians, and reptiles is close to the temperature of their environment. In contrast, birds and mammals have a stable body temperature that is often warmer than their environment.**

Most fishes, amphibians, and reptiles are ectotherms. An **ectotherm** is an animal whose body does not produce much internal heat—its body temperature changes depending on the temperature of its environment.

Birds and mammals are endotherms. An **endotherm** is an animal whose body regulates its own temperature by controlling the internal heat it produces. Endotherms have adaptations, such as sweat glands and fur or feathers, for maintaining their body temperature.

What Is a Vertebrate? (pp. 408–412)

This section explains the characteristics of chordates and vertebrates, the relationships of major groups of vertebrates, and the different ways they control their body temperature.

Use Target Reading Skills

When you compare and contrast, you examine the similarities and differences between things. Use the table below to compare and contrast the characteristics of chordates and the characteristics of vertebrates.

Chordates and Vertebrates

	Notochord	Nerve Cord	Slits in Throat Area
Chordates	a.	b.	c.
Vertebrates	d.	e.	f.

Characteristics of Chordates (pp. 408–409)

1. What characteristics do all chordates share?

    _____

    _____

    _____

2. A flexible rod that supports a chordate's back is called a(n)
    _____.

3. Is the following sentence true or false? In vertebrates, part or all of the notochord is replaced by a backbone. _____

4. Is the following sentence true or false? Gill slits disappear before birth in all chordates. _____

Structure and Function of Vertebrates • *Reading/Notetaking Guide*

Characteristics of Vertebrates (pp. 409–410)

5. The backbone is formed by many similar bones, called _____, which are lined up in a row.

6. A vertebrate's backbone is part of a(n) _____, or internal skeleton.

7. Complete the concept map to show the functions of the endoskeleton.

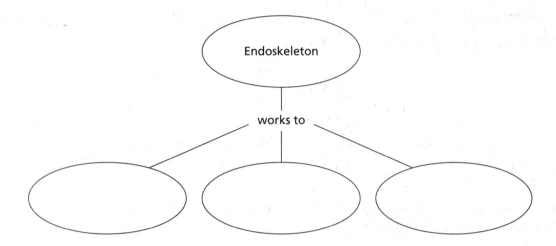

Evolution of Vertebrates (pp. 410–411)

8. How have scientists been able to infer the relationships between the major groups of vertebrates?

_____

_____

9. _____ were probably the first group of vertebrates.

10. Complete the sequence map to show the pattern of evolution in vertebrates.

Pattern of Vertebrate Evolution

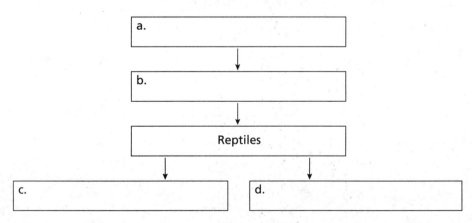

11. What was the latest group of vertebrates to arise?

_____

Structure and Function of Vertebrates · *Reading/Notetaking Guide*

What Is a Vertebrate? *(continued)*

Keeping Conditions Stable *(pp. 411–412)*

12. Circle the letter of each animal that has a body temperature close to the temperature of its environment.

    a. bird
    b. fish
    c. reptile
    d. mammal

13. What is an ectotherm?

    _____

    _____

    _____

14. Is the following sentence true or false? A turtle has the same body temperature when it's lying in the sun and when it's swimming in a cool river. _____

15. An animal whose body regulates its own temperature by controlling the internal heat it produces is a(n) _____.

16. Circle the letter of adaptations that help endotherms maintain their body temperature.

    a. spines
    b. fur
    c. sweat glands
    d. cartilage

17. Is the following sentence true or false? Ectotherms can live in a greater variety of environments than endotherms can.

    _____

Fishes

Key Concepts

- What are the characteristics of most fishes?

- What are the major groups of fishes and how do they differ?

A **fish** is a vertebrate that lives in water and uses fins to move. **In addition to living in water and having fins, most fishes are ectotherms, obtain oxygen through gills, and have scales.** Scales are thin, overlapping plates that cover the skin. Fishes are the largest group of vertebrates—nearly half of all vertebrate species are fishes.

Fishes get their oxygen from water. Water flows into a fish's mouth and over its gills. Gills are the main organs of a fish's respiratory system. Gills contain many blood vessels. As water flows over the gills, oxygen moves from the water into the fish's blood, while carbon dioxide, a waste product, moves out of the blood and into the water.

Like all vertebrates, fishes have a closed circulatory system. Fins help fishes swim. Fins provide large surfaces to push against the water. Most of the movements of fishes are related to obtaining food, but some are related to reproduction. Most fishes reproduce by external fertilization. The nervous system and sense organs of fish help them find food and avoid predators.

The major groups of fishes are jawless fishes, cartilaginous fishes, and bony fishes. Jawless fishes were the first vertebrates to appear on Earth. **Jawless fishes are unlike other fishes in that they have no jaws and no scales.** They feed by scraping, stabbing, and sucking their food. Their skeletons are made of **cartilage,** a tissue that is more flexible than bone. Hagfish and lampreys are the only kinds of jawless fishes.

Sharks, rays, and skates are cartilaginous fishes. **The cartilaginous fishes have jaws and scales, and skeletons made of cartilage.** Cartilaginous fishes are carnivores. Like all fishes, they obtain oxygen from water.

A bony fish has jaws, scales, a pocket on each side of the head that holds the gills, and a skeleton made of hard bones. A bony fish also has an organ called a **swim bladder,** an internal gas-filled sac that helps the fish stay stable at different depths in the water. Bony fishes make up about 95 percent of all fish species.

Structure and Function of Vertebrates · *Reading/Notetaking Guide*

Fishes (pp. 414–419)

This section describes the characteristics of most fishes and how the major groups of fishes differ.

Use Target Reading Skills

When you compare and contrast, you examine the similarities and differences between things. Use the table below to compare and contrast the characteristics of the three types of fishes.

Three Types of Fishes

	Jaws	Skeletons	Scales
Jawless Fishes	a.	b.	c.
Cartilaginous Fishes	d.	e.	f.
Bony Fishes	g.	h.	i.

Characteristics of Fishes (pp. 415–417)

1. What is a fish?

   _____

   _____

2. Circle the letter of each characteristic of fishes.

   a. gills
   b. endotherm
   c. scales
   d. ectotherm

3. Fishes get oxygen from _____ that moves through openings in the fish's throat region that lead to _____.

4. Most fishes have _____ fertilization; the eggs are fertilized outside of the female's body.

5. Circle the letter of each sentence that is true about fishes.

   a. Fins help fishes swim by providing a large surface area to push against water.
   b. Fishes have an open circulatory system.
   c. Fishes cannot see well in water.
   d. Fishes have keen senses of touch, smell, and taste to help them catch food.

6. Is the following sentence true or false? No fishes give birth to live young.

   _____

Diversity of Fishes (pp. 417–419)

7. List three groups of fishes.

   a. _____

   b. _____

   c. _____

8. Circle the letter of each sentence that is true about jawless fishes.

   a. Jawless fishes do not have scales.
   b. Jawless fishes have skeletons made of bones.
   c. Sharks are jawless fishes.
   d. Some jawless fishes are parasites.

9. The skeletons of cartilaginous fishes are made of

   _____.

10. Circle the letter of each characteristic of cartilaginous fishes.

    a. jaws
    b. skeletons made of cartilage
    c. scales
    d. bones

Structure and Function of Vertebrates ▪ *Reading/Notetaking Guide*

Fishes *(continued)*

11. Is the following sentence true or false? Cartilaginous fishes are all herbivores. _____

12. How do sharks obtain oxygen from water?

_____

_____

Match the parts of bony fishes with their functions.

Part	Function
_____ **13.** fins	**a.** Helps stabilize the fish at different depths in the water
_____ **14.** scales	**b.** Cover the body by overlapping each other
_____ **15.** gill pocket	**c.** Holds the gills
_____ **16.** swim bladder	**d.** Help the fish stay upright in the water

17. Bony fishes make up about _____ of all fish species.

Amphibians

Key Concepts

- What is the life cycle of an amphibian like?

- What are some adaptations of adult amphibians for living on land?

Salamanders, frogs, and toads are amphibians. An **amphibian** is an ectothermic vertebrate that spends its early life in water. **After beginning their lives in water, most amphibians spend their adulthood on land, returning to water to reproduce.**

Fertilized amphibian eggs develop in water. After a few days, larvae wriggle out of a jelly that coats the eggs and begin a free-swimming, fishlike life. The larvae of most amphibians grow and eventually undergo metamorphosis. Frog and toad larvae are called **tadpoles** and look very different from the adults. After the tadpole hatches, it begins to develop hind legs. Next, its front legs develop. Finally, the tail is absorbed, and development is complete. In contrast, the larvae of salamanders look like the adults.

The respiratory and circulatory systems of adult amphibians are adapted for life on land. In addition, adult amphibians have adaptations for moving. Amphibian larvae use gills to obtain oxygen, whereas adults use lungs. **Lungs** are organs of air-breathing vertebrates in which oxygen gas and carbon dioxide gas are exchanged between the air and blood. Amphibian larvae also have a single-loop circulatory system and two-chambered heart, like that of a fish. In contrast, the circulatory system of an adult amphibian has two loops and a heart with three chambers. The two upper chambers of the heart are called **atria,** and the lower chamber is the **ventricle.** Blood moves to the lungs in one loop and to the body in the other loop.

Most adult amphibians have strong skeletons and muscular limbs adapted for moving on land. Frogs and toads have powerful hind-leg muscles for jumping.

Amphibian populations are declining all over the world. One reason is the destruction of their habitats. A **habitat** is the specific environment in which an animal lives. Because their skins are delicate and their eggs lack shells, amphibians are especially sensitive to environmental changes. Poisons in the environment can pollute the waters that amphibians need to live and reproduce.

Structure and Function of Vertebrates • *Reading/Notetaking Guide*

Amphibians (pp. 420–423)

This section describes the life cycle of amphibians and some adaptations of adult amphibians for living on land.

Use Target Reading Skills

As you read, fill in the cycle diagram below to show the different stages of a frog's life cycle. Write each step of the process in a separate circle.

Frog Metamorphosis

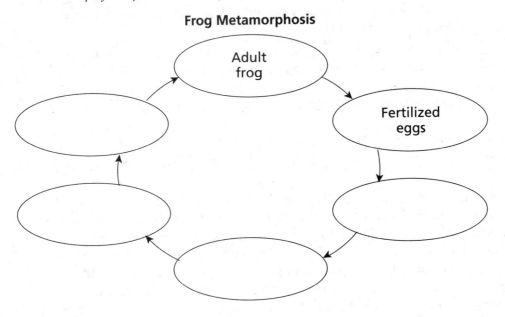

What Is an Amphibian? (pp. 420–421)

1. What is an amphibian?

_____

_____

Structure and Function of Vertebrates • *Reading/Notetaking Guide*

2. Amphibians with long, slender bodies that keep their tails as adults are called _____.

3. Is the following sentence true or false? Most amphibians undergo metamorphosis during development. _____

4. Complete the flowchart to show the steps in the metamorphosis of a frog.

Frog Metamorphosis

Fertilized eggs hatch and a legless _____ swims out.

↓

First, _____ legs develop.

↓

Then the tadpole develops _____ legs.

↓

The tail is completely gone when the frog is a(n) _____ .

Living on Land (pp. 422–423)

5. Circle the letter of each sentence that is true about adaptations for living on land.

   a. Adult amphibians have lungs.
   b. Adult amphibians have a two-chambered heart.
   c. Adult amphibians must have a strong skeleton to support the body against the pull of gravity.
   d. Adult amphibians have muscular limbs adapted for crawling on land.

6. How does the method of obtaining oxygen change during metamorphosis?

   _____

   _____

7. How is the circulatory system of a tadpole different from that of an adult amphibian?

   _____

   _____

Amphibians (continued)

8. How are frogs and toads adapted for hopping and leaping?

_____

_____

_____

9. An animal's _____ is the specific environment in which it lives.

10. The destruction of amphibian _____ is causing populations of amphibians to decrease.

11. Why are amphibians especially sensitive to changes in the environment?

_____

_____

Chapter 12 Structure and Function of Vertebrates • *Section 4 Summary*

Reptiles

Key Concepts
- What adaptations allow reptiles to live on land?
- What are the characteristics of each of the three main groups of reptiles?
- What environmental change may have caused the extinction of the dinosaurs?

A **reptile** is an ectothermic vertebrate that has lungs and scaly skin. Snakes, lizards, turtles, and alligators are all reptiles. **The skin, kidneys, and eggs of reptiles are adapted to conserve water.**

Reptiles have dry, tough skin covered with scales that protects them and helps keep water in their bodies. Reptiles also have **kidneys,** which are organs that filter wastes from the blood, excreting them in a watery fluid called **urine.** The kidneys of reptiles concentrate the urine so that the reptiles lose very little water.

Reptiles' eggs are fertilized internally. Unlike an amphibian's egg, a reptile's egg has a shell and membranes that protect the developing embryo and keep it from drying out. This type of egg is called an **amniotic egg.**

Both lizards and snakes are reptiles that have skin covered with overlapping scales. As they grow, they shed their skin and scales, replacing the worn ones with new ones. Lizards have four legs. Snakes have no legs and move by contracting bands of muscles that are connected to their ribs and backbone. Most lizards are carnivores that capture their prey by jumping at it. All snakes are carnivores. Most feed on small mammals, such as mice. However, some snakes eat large prey. A snake's jawbones can spread wide apart, and its skin stretches, too.

Alligators, crocodiles, and their relatives are the largest living reptiles. **Both alligators and crocodiles are large, carnivorous reptiles that care for their young.**

A turtle is a reptile whose body is covered by a protective shell that includes the ribs and the backbone. Some turtles can pull their legs and head into their shells for protection. Turtles have sharp-edged beaks instead of teeth. While some turtles are carnivores, other turtles are herbivores.

Dinosaurs were a major group of reptiles that died out 65 million years ago. Dinosaurs were the earliest vertebrates that had legs positioned directly beneath their bodies. This adaptation allowed them to move more easily than animals like salamanders and lizards. Most herbivorous dinosaurs walked on four legs. Most carnivorous dinosaurs ran on two legs.

Climate changes may have caused the extinction of dinosaurs and other organisms. Scientists hypothesize that Earth became much cooler because huge clouds of dust and gas blocked sunlight. The dinosaurs did not have adaptations that let them survive.

Structure and Function of Vertebrates ▪ *Reading/Notetaking Guide*

Reptiles (pp. 424–431)

This section describes adaptations that enable reptiles to live their entire lives on land. It also explains the characteristics of the major groups of reptiles and what may have caused the extinction of dinosaurs.

Use Target Reading Skills

When you compare and contrast, you examine the similarities and differences between things. Use the table below to compare and contrast the characteristics of alligators and snakes.

Alligators and Snakes

	How They Move	What They Eat	Whether They Care for Their Young
Alligators	a.	b.	c.
Snakes	d.	e.	f.

Structure and Function of Vertebrates ▪ *Reading/Notetaking Guide*

Adaptations for Life on Land (pp. 425–426)

1. What is a reptile?

   _____

   _____

2. Circle the letter of the animal that is NOT a reptile.
   a. snake
   b. alligator
   c. lizard
   d. salamander

3. Is the following sentence true or false? Reptiles were the first vertebrates to be well adapted to live their entire lives on land.

   _____

4. Reptiles get their oxygen from the _____, and they breathe entirely with _____.

5. What are two functions of a reptile's scaly skin?

   _____

   _____

6. How do the kidneys keep reptiles from losing water?

   _____

   _____

7. What adaptations does a reptile's egg have to keep it from drying out?

   _____

   _____

   _____

Diversity of Reptiles (pp. 427–430)

8. What characteristics do both lizards and snakes have?

   _____

   _____

   _____

   _____

9. Circle the letter of each characteristic that snakes have.
   a. no legs
   b. jawbones that spread wide apart
   c. no lungs
   d. teeth that help them capture prey

Structure and Function of Vertebrates ▪ *Reading/Notetaking Guide*

Reptiles *(continued)*

10. Is the following sentence true or false? All snakes are carnivores.

_____

11. Is the following sentence true or false? All snakes have venom glands.

_____

12. Describe how snakes move.

_____

_____

_____

13. Is the following sentence true or false? Alligators, crocodiles, and their relatives are the largest living reptiles. _____

14. Complete the Venn diagram to show the similarities and differences between alligators and crocodiles.

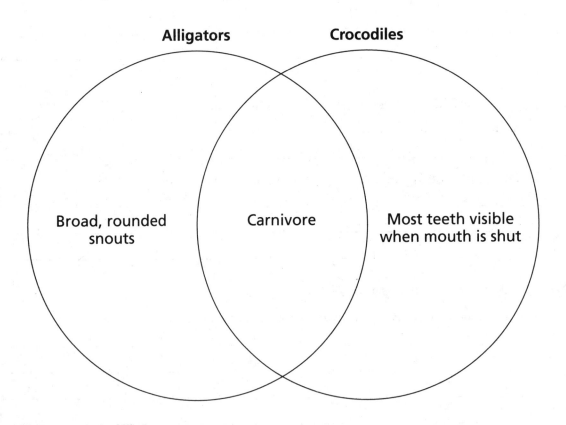

Alligators   **Crocodiles**

Broad, rounded snouts   Carnivore   Most teeth visible when mouth is shut

15. How do alligators and crocodiles care for their young?

_____

_____

Structure and Function of Vertebrates • *Reading/Notetaking Guide*

16. What is a turtle?

_____

_____

17. Is the following sentence true or false? All turtles can pull their head, legs, and tail inside their shell. _____

18. Instead of teeth, turtles have sharp-edged _____.

Extinct Reptiles—The Dinosaurs (p. 394)

19. Circle the letter of each sentence that is true about dinosaurs.

  a. They became extinct about 65 million years ago.
  b. Some dinosaurs might have been endotherms.
  c. Dinosaurs were the earliest vertebrates to have legs positioned directly under their bodies.
  d. Most carnivorous dinosaurs walked on four legs.

20. What might have caused the extinction of dinosaurs?

_____

_____

_____

Birds

Key Concept

■ What are the main characteristics of birds?

A bird is an endothermic vertebrate that has feathers and a four-chambered heart. A bird also lays eggs. The bodies of birds are adapted for flight. For example, many bones in the bird's body are hollow, which makes the skeleton light. The bones of a bird's front limbs form wings. Flying birds have large chest muscles. And all birds have feathers.

Contour feathers are large feathers that give shape to a bird's body. The contour feathers that extend beyond the body on the wings and tail help it balance and steer during flight. Birds also have short, fluffy **down feathers** that are found against the skin and keep the bird warm.

Flying takes a lot of energy. Birds have a system of air sacs inside their bodies that connect to their lungs. Air sacs enable birds to get more oxygen from each breath than other animals can.

A bird's heart has four chambers. There is no mixing of oxygen-rich and oxygen-poor blood in a four-chambered heart.

Birds have no teeth. Instead, they have bills that are adapted to the type of food they eat. For example, a hawk has a pointy, curved bill that acts like a meat hook.

Many birds have an internal storage tank, or **crop,** that allows them to store food inside the body after swallowing it. Birds also have a stomach where food is bathed in chemicals that help to break it down. This food then moves into a thick-walled, muscular part of the stomach, the **gizzard,** which squeezes and grinds the food.

Birds need a lot of energy to maintain their body temperature. Each day, an average bird eats the amount of food equal to about a quarter of its body weight. Feathers also help birds maintain their body temperature.

Birds have internal fertilization and lay eggs. Bird eggs will develop only at a temperature close to the body temperature of the parent. Most parent birds care for their young at least until they are able to fly.

Birds (pp. 432–437)

This section tells about the characteristics of birds, how they care for their young, and about their special adaptations.

Use Target Reading Skills

Preview the figure titled Adaptations for Flight *in your text. Then write two questions that you have about the diagram in the graphic organizer below. As you read, answer your questions.*

Adaptations for Flight

Q.
A.
Q.
A.

Characteristics of Birds (pp. 433–437)

1. List five characteristics of birds.

   a. _____ b. _____

   c. _____ d. _____

   e. _____

2. Circle the letter of each adaptation that enables birds to fly.

   a. feathers
   b. hollow bones
   c. scales
   d. large chest muscles

Name _____ Date _____ Class _____

Structure and Function of Vertebrates • *Reading/Notetaking Guide*

Birds *(continued)*

Match the bird feathers with their characteristics. Each kind of feather may be used more than once.

Characteristics

Feathers

____ 3. Traps air to keep bird from losing heat

a. contour feather

b. down feather

____ 4. Balances and steers bird in flight

____ 5. Found right next to a bird's skin

____ 6. Gives shape to a bird's body

7. Which feather below is a contour feather, and which is a down feather?

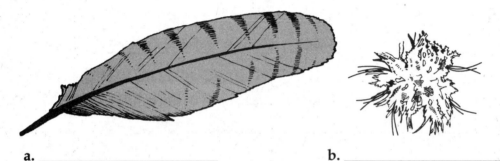

a. _____ b. _____

8. Why do birds pull their feathers through their bills?

_____

_____

9. What is the function of air sacs?

_____

_____

_____

10. The right side of a bird's heart pumps blood to the _____.

The left side of a bird's heart pumps blood to the _____.

11. What is the advantage of a four-chambered heart?

_____

_____

_____

Structure and Function of Vertebrates ▪ *Reading/Notetaking Guide*

12. Circle the letter of each sentence that is true about birds.

   a. Birds have teeth.
   b. Each bird species has a bill shaped to help it get food quickly and efficiently.
   c. The crop stores food in the body after the bird swallows it.
   d. Chemicals break down food in the gizzard.

13. What is the function of a gizzard?

   _____

14. Why do birds need a lot of energy?

   _____

   _____

15. Cells must have enough _____ to release the energy from food.

16. Circle the letter of a characteristic of bird eggs.

   a. soft shell
   b. leathery shell
   c. hard shell
   d. no shell

17. In most bird species, the female lays the eggs in a(n)

   _____.

18. How do birds keep their eggs warm so that they will develop?

   _____

   _____

19. How long do parent birds care for their young?

   _____

Mammals

Key Concepts

- What characteristics do all mammals share?

- What are the main groups of mammals and how do they differ in their reproduction?

Mammals are a diverse group of vertebrates that share many characteristics. **All mammals are endothermic vertebrates that have a four-chambered heart and skin covered with fur or hair. Most mammals are born alive, and every young mammal is fed with milk produced by organs in its mother's body.** These organs are called **mammary glands.** In addition, mammals have teeth of different shapes that are adapted to the type of food they eat. Most mammals have teeth of four different shapes to tear and chew their food. Incisors are flat-edged teeth used to bite off and cut parts of food. Canines are sharply pointed teeth that stab food and tear into it. Premolars and molars grind and shred food into tiny bits.

Mammals breathe with lungs. Mammals breathe in and out because of the combined action of rib muscles and a large muscle called the **diaphragm** located at the bottom of the ribs. The lungs have a huge, moist surface area where oxygen can move into the blood. Mammals have a four-chambered heart and a two-loop circulatory system.

All mammals have fur or hair at some point in their lives. Mammals in cold climates usually have thicker fur than those that live in warm climates.

Mammals have adaptations that allow them to move in more ways than other vertebrates. Also, the brains of mammals enable them to sense their environment and behave in complex ways. The senses of mammals are highly developed and adapted for the ways that individual species live.

There are three main groups of mammals—monotremes, marsupials, and placental mammals. The groups differ in how they reproduce and how their young develop.

Monotremes are mammals that lay eggs. There are three species of monotremes—two species of spiny anteaters plus the duck-billed platypus.

Marsupials are mammals whose young are born at a very early stage of development. They usually continue to develop in a pouch on their mother's body. Koalas, kangaroos, and opossums are some of the better-known marsupials. Marsupials have a very short **gestation period,** which is the length of time between fertilization and birth.

Most mammals, including humans, are **placental mammals.** A placental mammal develops inside its mother's body until its body systems can function independently. The **placenta** is an organ in pregnant female mammals that passes materials such as food and oxygen from the mother to the developing embryo and carries the embryo's wastes away. Young mammals typically stay with their mothers or both parents for an extended period of time to learn how to survive.

Structure and Function of Vertebrates ▪ *Reading/Notetaking Guide*

Mammals (pp. 438–444)

This section describes the characteristics of mammals and how they differ in their reproduction.

Use Target Reading Skills

When you compare and contrast, you examine the similarities and differences between things. Use the table below to compare and contrast how monotremes, marsupials, and placental mammals reproduce and develop their young.

Monotremes, Marsupials, and Placental Mammals

	How They Reproduce	How They Develop Their Young	Gestation Period
Monotremes	a.	b.	c.
Marsupials	d.	e.	f.
Placental Mammals	g.	h.	i.

Characteristics of Mammals (pp. 439–441)

1. Circle the letter of each characteristic of mammals.

   a. endothermic vertebrate   **b.** feathers

   c. three-chambered heart   **d.** teeth

2. Is the following sentence true or false? The young of most mammals are born alive. _____

3. Every young mammal is fed with _____ produced in its mother's body.

Match the type of teeth with their function. Some functions may be used more than once.

Teeth	Function
_____ 4. canines	a. Bite off and cut parts of food
_____ 5. molars	b. Stab food and tear it
_____ 6. incisors	c. Grind and shred food into tiny bits
_____ 7. premolars	

Structure and Function of Vertebrates • *Reading/Notetaking Guide*

Mammals *(continued)*

8. Look at the teeth in the diagram above. Is this animal an herbivore or a carnivore? How do you know?

   _____

   _____

9. Mammals breathe in and out because of the combined action of rib muscles and a large muscle called the _____ located at the bottom of the ribs.

10. Circle the letter of the number of chambers in a mammal's heart.
    a. two
    b. three
    c. four
    d. five

11. Is the following sentence true or false? All mammals have fur or hair at some point in their lives. _____

12. How do fur and hair help mammals?

    _____

    _____

    _____

13. Generally, animals in cold regions have _____ coats of fur than animals in warmer environments.

14. Most mammals have four _____ and can walk and run.

Match the type of mammal with its specialized way of moving.

Mammal	Way of Moving
____ 15. bats	a. Have flippers for swimming
____ 16. dolphins	b. Have wings for flying
____ 17. orangutans	c. Swing by their arms

18. What sense do bats use to capture insects?

    _____

    _____

Structure and Function of Vertebrates · *Reading/Notetaking Guide*

Diversity of Mammals (pp. 442–444)

19. The three main groups of mammals are _____,
_____, and _____.

20. Is the following sentence true or false? Marsupials are mammals that lay
eggs. _____

21. Circle the letter of each animal that is a placental mammal.

    a. kangaroo
    b. elephant
    c. duck-billed platypus
    d. chimpanzee

22. What is the function of the placenta?

_____

_____

23. What is a gestation period?

_____

24. Why do young mammals usually stay with their mother or both parents
for an extended period of time?

_____

_____

Chapter 13 Bones and Muscles • *Section 1 Summary*

Organ Systems and Homeostasis

Key Concepts

- What are the levels of organization in the body?

- What systems are in the human body, and what are their functions?

- What is homeostasis?

   The levels of organization in the human body consist of cells, tissues, organs, and organ systems. A cell is the basic unit of structure and function in a living thing. Cells perform the basic processes that keep organisms alive. The nucleus is the control center that directs the cell's activities and contains information that determines the cell's characteristics. The area between the cell membrane and the nucleus is called the **cytoplasm.**

   A **tissue** is a group of specialized cells that perform the same function. The human body contains four basic types of tissue: muscle tissue, nerve tissue, connective tissue, and epithelial tissue. **Muscle tissue** can contract, or shorten. This tissue is what makes parts of your body move. **Nervous tissue** carries messages back and forth between the brain and every other part of the body. It directs and controls the body. **Connective tissue** provides support for your body and connects all its parts. Bone, fat, and blood are all connective tissues. **Epithelial tissue** covers the surfaces of your body. The skin and the lining of the digestive system are examples of epithelial tissue.

   An organ is a structure that is composed of different kinds of tissue and does a specific job. Each organ in your body is part of an organ system. An **organ system** is a group of organs that work together to perform a major function. **The human body has eleven organ systems. The skeletal, muscular, and integumentary systems provide structure and allow movement. The circulatory, respiratory, digestive, excretory, immune, and reproductive systems carry out the processes of life. The nervous and endocrine systems provide control over body processes.** For each system to function, its organs and tissues must work together. And so must its cells.

   All the systems of the body work together to maintain **homeostasis,** the body's tendency to keep an internal balance. **Homeostasis is the process by which an organism's internal environment is kept stable in spite of changes in the external environment.** Sometimes, things can happen to throw off homeostasis. As a result, your heart may beat more rapidly or your breathing may quicken. These are signs of **stress,** the reaction of your body to potentially threatening, challenging, or disturbing events. When the stress is over, homeostasis is restored, and the body returns to its normal state.

Bones and Muscles ▪ *Reading/Notetaking Guide*

Organic Systems and Homeostasis (pp. 500–509)

This section tells how the body is organized and describes the systems in the human body and their functions.

Use Target Reading Skills

As you read, take notes on the main ideas and important details. Consider the Key Concepts and Key Terms. Use the graphic organizer below to take notes.

Recall Clues and Questions	Notes
What are the levels of organization in the body?	

Bones and Muscles ▪ *Reading/Notetaking Guide*

Organs Systems and Homeostasis *(continued)*

Introduction (p. 500)

1. List the levels of organization in the human body, starting with the smallest unit.

   a. _____   b. _____

   c. _____   d. _____

Cells (p. 501)

2. The basic unit of structure and function in a living thing is a(n) _____.

3. Circle the letter of the outside boundary of an animal cell.
   a. cytoplasm
   b. nucleus
   c. tissue
   d. cell membrane

4. The control center that directs the cell's activities and contains information that determines the cell's form and function is the _____.

5. What is the cytoplasm?

   _____

   _____

   _____

6. Is the following sentence true or false? Cells carry on the processes that keep organisms alive. _____

Tissues (p. 502)

7. What is a tissue?

   _____

   _____

Bones and Muscles · *Reading/Notetaking Guide*

8. Complete the table to show the functions and examples of the tissues in the human body.

Tissues in the Human Body		
Tissue	**Function**	**Example**
Muscle		
Nervous		
Connective		
Epithelial		

Organs and Organ Systems (pp. 502–507)

9. A structure that is made up of different kinds of tissues and does a specific job is a(n) _____.

10. Circle the letter of the unit of organization that represents an organ.

   a. muscle cell
   b. blood
   c. heart
   d. digestive system

Bones and Muscles • *Reading/Notetaking Guide*

Organexity Systems and Homeostasis *(continued)*

11. Is the following sentence true or false? An organ has a specific job that is more complex than that of a tissue. _____

12. What is an organ system?

_____

_____

Match the organ system with its function.

Organ Systems	**Functions**
____ 13. endocrine	a. Takes oxygen into the body
____ 14. circulatory	b. Supports and protects the body
____ 15. excretory	c. Removes wastes
____ 16. respiratory	d. Controls body process by means of chemicals
____ 17. digestive	e. Takes food into the body and breaks it down
____ 18. skeletal	f. Transports materials to and from body cells
____ 19. muscular	g. Takes in information from the environment and from within the body and commands the body to respond
____ 20. integumentary	
____ 21. immune	h. Protects the body from disease-causing bacteria and viruses
____ 22. reproductive	i. Protects the body from injury and disease and helps regulate body temperature
____ 23. nervous	j. Contains organs that produce sex cells
	k. Works to move the body by pulling on the skeleton

Homeostasis *(pp. 508–509)*

24. The process by which an organism's internal environment is kept stable in spite of changes in the external environment is called

_____ .

25. How does your body maintain a constant temperature on a hot day?

_____

_____

26. What is stress?

_____

The Skeletal System

Key Concepts

- What are the functions of the skeleton?

- What role do joints play in the body?

- What are the characteristics of bone, and how can you keep your bones strong and healthy?

The **skeleton** is made up of all the bones in one's body. **Your skeleton has five major functions. It provides shape and support, enables you to move, protects your organs, produces blood cells, and stores minerals and other materials until your body needs them.** The backbone, or vertebral column, is the center of the skeleton. The backbone is made up of 26 small bones, or **vertebrae** (singular *vertebra*). If your backbone were just one bone, you would not be able to bend or twist.

A **joint** is a place in the body where two bones come together. **Joints allow bones to move in different ways.** Immovable joints connect bones in a way that allows little or no movement. Movable joints allow the body to make a wide range of movements. The bones in movable joints are held together by a strong connective tissue called a **ligament. Cartilage** is a connective tissue that is more flexible than bone. Cartilage covers the ends of the bones and keeps them from rubbing against each other.

Bones are complex living structures that undergo growth and development. A thin, tough membrane covers all of a bone except the ends. Blood vessels and nerves enter and leave the bone through the membrane. Beneath the membrane is a layer of **compact bone,** which is hard and dense, but not solid. Small canals run through the compact bone, carrying blood vessels and nerves from the bone's surface to the living cells within the bone. Just inside the compact bone is a layer of **spongy bone,** which has many small spaces within it. Spongy bone is also found at the ends of the bone. The spaces in bone contain a soft connective tissue called **marrow.** There are two types of marrow—red and yellow. Red bone marrow produces blood cells. Yellow marrow stores fat that serves as an energy reserve.

The bones of your skeleton are both strong and lightweight. Bones are hard because they are made up of two minerals—phosphorus and calcium. New bone tissue forms continually throughout your life.

A combination of a balanced diet and regular exercise are important for a lifetime of healthy bones. As people become older, their bones begin to lose some minerals. Mineral loss can lead to **osteoporosis,** a condition in which the body's bones become weak and break easily. Regular exercise and a diet rich in calcium can help prevent osteoporosis.

Bones and Muscles ▪ *Reading/Notetaking Guide*

The Skeletal System (pp. 510–517)

This section describes the skeletal system and its function. It also tells how to keep your bones strong and healthy.

Use Target Reading Skills

As you read, take notes on the main ideas and important details. Consider the Key Concepts and Key Terms. Use the graphic organizer below to take notes.

The Skeletal System

Recall Clues and Questions	Notes
What does the skeleton do?	

Functions of the Skeletal System (pp. 510–512)

1. List the five major functions of the skeleton.

   a. _____

   b. _____

   c. _____

   d. _____

   e. _____

Bones and Muscles ▪ *Reading/Notetaking Guide*

2. Circle the letter of the bone that makes up the center of the skeleton.
   a. skull
   b. pelvic girdle
   c. backbone
   d. femur

3. The 26 small bones that make up the backbone are the _____.

4. How does the skeleton help the body move?

   _____

   _____

   _____

5. Circle the letter of the bones that protect the brain.
   a. backbone
   b. pelvic girdle
   c. ribs
   d. skull

6. The long bones of the arms and legs make _____.

Joints of the Skeleton (pp. 512–513)

7. What is a joint?

   _____

   _____

8. What are the two kinds of joints in the body?

   a. _____ b. _____

9. Circle the letter of bones that are held together by immovable joints.
   a. knee
   b. ankle
   c. skull
   d. wrist

The Skeletal System *(continued)*

10. Complete the table to show the four types of movable joints.

Movable Joints		
Joint	**Kind of Motion**	**Where It's Found in the Body**
Hinge		
Ball-and-socket		
Pivot		
Sliding		

11. The bones in movable joints are held together by strong connective tissues called _____.

Bones—Strong and Living (pp. 514–516)

12. Circle the letter of each sentence that is true about bones.

    a. Bones are very strong and lightweight.
    b. Concrete can absorb more force without breaking than bone can.
    c. Bones make up over half of an adult's body weight.
    d. Bones are hard because they contain minerals.

13. When do bone cells form new bone tissue?

_____

_____

_____

Bones and Muscles ▪ *Reading/Notetaking Guide*

14. Label the parts of the bone in the diagram below.

a. _____

b. _____

c. _____

d. _____

Match each part of a bone with its characteristics.

Bone Parts

_____ **15.** marrow

_____ **16.** outer membrane

_____ **17.** compact bone

_____ **18.** spongy bone

Characteristics

a. Where blood vessels and nerves enter and leave the bone

b. Has small canals with blood vessels running through

c. Strong, but lightweight because it has many small spaces within it

d. Soft connective tissue in the spaces in bone

19. Is the following statement true or false? Cartilage is a type of connective tissue that is more flexible than bone. _____

20. Circle the letter of each sentence that is true about how bones form.

a. Much of an infant's skeleton is bone.
b. As the body grows, the cartilage in the skeleton is replaced with hard bone tissue.
c. By the time the body stops growing, all of the cartilage has been replaced with bone.
d. Cartilage covers the ends of many bones in the body of an adult.

Taking Care of Your Bones (pp. 516–517)

21. What can you do to keep your bones healthy? _____

_____

_____

22. A condition in which the body's bones become weak and break easily is called _____.

The Muscular System

Key Concepts

■ What types of muscles are found in the body?

■ Why do skeletal muscles work in pairs?

There are about 600 muscles in your body. The muscles that are not under your conscious control are called **involuntary muscles.** Involuntary muscles are responsible for activities such as breathing and digesting food. The muscles that are under your control are called **voluntary muscles.** Smiling and turning the pages in a book are actions of voluntary muscles.

Your body has three types of muscle tissue—skeletal muscle, smooth muscle, and cardiac muscle. Some of these muscle tissues are involuntary, and some are voluntary. Skeletal muscles are attached to the bones of your skeleton. At the end of a skeletal muscle is a tendon. A **tendon** is a strong connective tissue that attaches muscle to bone. Because you have conscious control of skeletal muscles, they are classified as voluntary muscles. These muscles provide the force that moves your bones. Skeletal muscles react quickly and tire quickly. Skeletal muscle cells appear banded, or striated. For this reason, they are sometimes called **striated muscles.**

Smooth muscles are called involuntary muscles because they work automatically. They are inside many internal organs of the body and control many types of movements inside your body, such as those involved in the process of digestion. Smooth muscles react more slowly and tire more slowly than skeletal muscles. **Cardiac muscles** are involuntary muscles found only in the heart. Cardiac muscles do not get tired.

Muscles work by contracting, or becoming shorter and thicker. **Because muscle cells can only contract, not extend, skeletal muscles must work in pairs. While one muscle contracts, the other muscle in the pair relaxes to its original length.** For example, in order to move the lower arm, the biceps muscle on the front of the upper arm contracts to bend the elbow. This lifts the forearm and hand. As the biceps contracts, the triceps on the back of the upper arm returns to its original length. To straighten the elbow, the triceps muscle contracts while the biceps returns to its original length.

Exercise is important for maintaining both muscular strength and flexibility. Exercise makes individual muscle cells grow wider, thicker, and stronger. Sometimes, muscle injuries such as strains and cramps, can occur. Resting the injured area can help it heal.

Bones and Muscles · *Reading/Notetaking Guide*

The Muscular System (pp. 518–522)

This section tells about the three kinds of muscle tissue in the human body and how muscles work to move the body.

Use Target Reading Skills

As you read, take notes on the main ideas and important details. Consider the Key Concepts and Key Terms. Use the graphic organizer below to take notes.

Recall Clues and Questions	Notes
What are the three types of muscle?	

Types of Muscle (pp. 518–520)

1. List the two groups of muscles in the body and describe how they are controlled.

   a. _____

   b. _____

2. Circle the letter of the action that is controlled by involuntary muscles.

   a. smiling
   b. breathing
   c. walking
   d. standing up

Bones and Muscles · *Reading/Notetaking Guide*

The Muscular System *(continued)*

3. Complete the table to compare and contrast the three types of muscle tissue in the body.

Types of Muscles			
Muscles	Location in Body	Voluntary or Involuntary	Striated or Not
Skeletal			
	Inside many internal organs		
Cardiac			

4. A strong connective tissue that attaches muscles to bone is a(n) _____.

5. Is the following sentence true or false? Skeletal muscles react quickly and tire easily. _____

6. The repeated contractions of cardiac muscle are called _____.

Muscles at Work (pp. 521–522)

7. When do muscles contract, or become shorter and thicker?

   _____

   _____

   _____

8. Is the following sentence true or false? Muscle cells can extend, or get longer, as well as contract, or get shorter. _____

9. Why must skeletal muscles work in pairs to move a bone?

   _____

   _____

   _____

   _____

   _____

10. To bend the elbow, the biceps muscle _____ and the triceps muscle relaxes to its _____.

Machines and the Body

Key Concepts

- How can you calculate how much work you do?

- How does a lever make work easier?

- How are levers classified?

- What joints are examples of fulcrums for levers in the body?

To understand how parts of your body act like machines, you first need to know about two concepts: force and work. A **force** is a push or pull. You do **work** when you exert a force on an object that causes the object to move some distance in the same direction as the force. **You can calculate the amount of work done on an object by multiplying force times distance.** A **machine** is a device that allows you to do work in a way that is easier or more effective.

One type of simple machine is a lever. A **lever** is a rigid rod that is free to rotate around a fixed pivot point. The fixed point that a lever rotates around is called the **fulcrum.** You can use a lever to turn a small force into a large force. **A lever makes work easier by changing the amount of force you exert, the distance over which you exert your force, or the direction in which you exert your force.** The force that you exert on the lever is called the **effort force.** The distance you push down on a lever is called the **effort resistance.** The force that the lever exerts on an object is called the **resistance force.** The distance the lever pushes up on an object is called the **resistance distance.** If you compare the effort force to the resistance force, you can find the advantage of using a lever. A lever's mechanical advantage is the number of times a lever increases a force exerted on it. The **mechanical advantage** of a lever is equal to the ratio of resistance force to the effort force. The distance from the fulcrum to the effort force is called the **effort arm,** and the distance from the fulcrum to the resistance force is called the resistance arm.

Levers are classified according to the location of the fulcrum relative to the effort and resistance forces. In a first-class lever, the fulcrum is located between the effort force and the resistance force. In a second-class lever, the resistance force is located between the fulcrum and the effort force. In a third-class lever, the effort force is located between the fulcrum and the resistance force.

When you move a part of your body, such as your legs, hips, hand, or head, you are using a lever system to perform the movement. Most of the machines in your body are levers that consist of bones and muscles. The most common lever in your body is the third-class lever, but your body also has first-class and second-class levers. The effort force is applied at the point at which a muscle attaches to the bone that serves as the lever. The resistance force is the force the bone exerts.

Many of the body's movable joints are actually the fulcrums of levers. The joints in the body act as pivot points for the bones acting as levers, and muscles provide the force. **The thigh joint, the wrist joint, the shoulder joint, the knee joint, and the elbow joint are examples of fulcrums for levers in the body.**

Bones and Muscles · *Reading/Notetaking Guide*

Machines and the Body (pp. 524–531)

This section explains how a lever makes work easier, how levers are classified, and what joints are examples of fulcrums for levers in the body.

Use Target Reading Skills

As you read, take notes on the main ideas and important details. Consider the Key Concepts and Key Terms. Use the graphic organizer below to take notes.

Recall Clues and Questions	Notes
What is a machine?	

Force and Work (p. 525)

1. When you do _____, you exert a _____ on an object that causes the object to move some distance in the same direction as the _____.

2. How can you calculate the amount of work done on an object?

   _____

3. What is a machine?

   _____

   _____

4. Is the following sentence true or false? A machine increases the amount of work needed to do a job. _____

Bones and Muscles · *Reading/Notetaking Guide*

Levers (pp. 526–529)

5. What is a lever?

   _____

   _____

6. The fixed point that a lever pivots around is called the

   _____.

7. Circle the letter of each sentence that is true about levers.
   a. A lever increases your effort force.
   b. There are three different types of levers.
   c. A lever changes the direction of your effort force.
   d. The fulcrum is always located at the same place on a lever.

Match the term with its definition.

Term		Definition
____	**8.** effort force	**a.** force that the lever exerts on an object
____	**9.** effort resistance	**b.** force that you exert on the lever
____	**10.** resistance force	**c.** distance the lever pushes up on an object
____	**11.** resistance distance	**d.** distance you push down on a lever

12. On each diagram below, draw a triangle below the lever to show where the fulcrum is located on each class of lever.

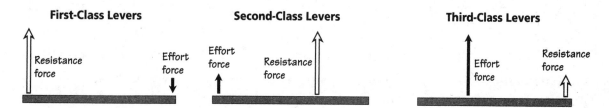

First-Class Levers Resistance force Effort force

Second-Class Levers Effort force Resistance force

Third-Class Levers Effort force Resistance force

13. Complete the following table about levers.

Levers	
Class of Lever	**Examples**
	Door, wheel barrow, bottle opener
	Seesaw, scissors, pliers
	Baseball bat, shovel, fishing pole

Bones and Muscles ▪ *Reading/Notetaking Guide*

Machines and the Body *(continued)*

14. What formula is used to calculate the mechanical advantage of a lever?

_____

Machines in the Body (pp. 530–531)

15. Most of the machines in your body are _____ that consist of _____.

16. List four examples of body parts that act as a lever system.

a. _____

b. _____

c. _____

d. _____

17. Explain the effort force and resistance force in a bone and muscle lever system.

_____

_____

18. List five joints that act as fulcrums for levers in the body.

a. _____

b. _____

c. _____

d. _____

e. _____

19. On the illustration of a living lever, label each arrow to show where the effort force and the resistance force are located. Also show where the fulcrum is located.

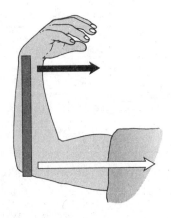

The Body's Transport System

Key Concepts

- What are the functions of the cardiovascular system?

- What is the function and structure of the heart?

- What path does blood take through the cardiovascular system?

- What are the functions and structures of arteries, capillaries, and veins?

The **cardiovascular system**—which consists of the heart, blood vessels, and blood—**carries needed substances to cells and carries waste products away from cells. In addition, blood contains cells that fight disease.** The **heart** is a hollow, muscular organ that pumps blood throughout the body. **Each time the heart beats, it pushes blood through the blood vessels of the cardiovascular system.** The heart has a right side and a left side. **The right side of the heart is completely separated from the left side by a wall of tissue called the septum.** Each side has two compartments, or chambers—an upper chamber and a lower chamber. Each upper chamber, or **atrium,** receives blood that comes into the heart. Located in the right atrium is the **pacemaker,** a group of cells that send out signals that make the heart muscle contract. Each lower chamber, or **ventricle,** pumps blood out of the heart. The atrium and ventricle are separated by a **valve,** a flap of tissue that prevents blood from flowing backward.

Blood travels through three kinds of blood vessels. **Arteries** carry blood away from the heart and into the capillaries. **Capillaries** are tiny vessels where substances are exchanged between the blood and body cells. **Veins** carry blood back to the heart.

The overall pattern of the body's blood flow consists of two loops. **In the first loop, blood travels from the heart to the lungs and then back to the heart. In the second loop, blood is pumped from the heart through the body and then returns again to the heart.** When blood leaves the heart, it travels through arteries. The right ventricle pumps blood into arteries that go to the lungs. The left ventricle pumps blood into the **aorta,** the largest artery in the body. Every organ receives blood from arteries that branch off the aorta. The **coronary arteries** carry blood to the heart itself. **The walls of arteries are generally very thick. In fact, artery walls consist of three cell layers.** The **pulse** you feel on the inside of your wrist is caused by the alternating expansion and relaxation of the artery wall.

Blood eventually flows from arteries into capillaries. **In the capillaries, materials are exchanged between the blood and the body's cells. Capillary walls are only one cell thick.** One way in which materials are exchanged is by diffusion. In **diffusion,** molecules move from an area where they are highly concentrated to an area where they are less concentrated.

After blood moves through capillaries, it enters larger blood vessels called veins, which carry blood back to the heart. The walls of veins, like those of arteries, have three layers with muscle in the middle layer.

Blood exerts a force, called **blood pressure,** against the walls of blood vessels. It is caused by the force with which the ventricles contract.

Circulation and Respiration ▪ *Reading/Notetaking Guide*

The Body's Transport System (pp. 538–547)

This section describes how the heart, blood vessels, and blood work together to carry materials throughout the body.

Use Target Reading Skills

As you read, complete the cycle diagram below that shows the path that blood follows as it circulates through the body. Write each step of the pathway in a separate circle.

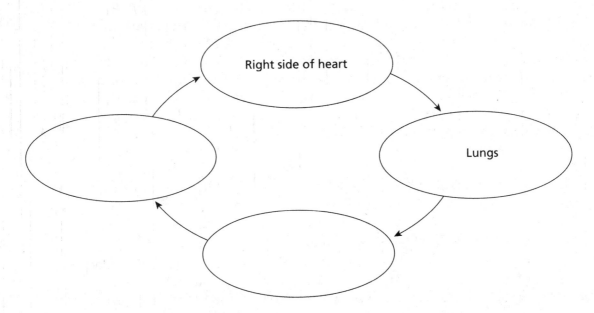

The Cardiovascular System (pp. 538–539)

1. Another name for the cardiovascular system is the
   _____ system.

2. Complete this concept map to show what makes up the cardiovascular system.

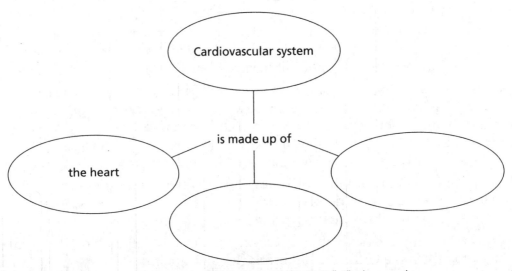

Circulation and Respiration • *Reading/Notetaking Guide*

3. What three things are carried throughout the body by the cardiovascular system?

    _____

    _____

The Heart (pp. 540–541)

4. Each time the heart beats, what does it do to blood?

    _____

    _____

5. Complete the table about the chambers of the heart.

Chambers of the Heart		
Questions	**Upper Chambers**	**Lower Chambers**
What are these chambers called?		
How many are there?		
What is the function, or job, of these chambers?		

6. A flap of tissue that prevents blood from flowing backward is a(n)
    _____.

7. The group of cells that adjusts the speed of the heart beat is called the
    _____.

8. When blood flows through the heart, what force pushes the blood out of the heart and into the arteries?

    _____

    _____

Circulation and Respiration • *Reading/Notetaking Guide*

The Body's Transport System *(continued)*

A Two-Loop System *(pp. 542–543)*

9. Name the three kinds of blood vessels.

_____

_____

10. Describe the loop in which the blood picks up oxygen.

_____

_____

_____

_____

11. Draw arrows on the diagram below to show how blood circulates through the body. The first arrow should start in the right atrium.

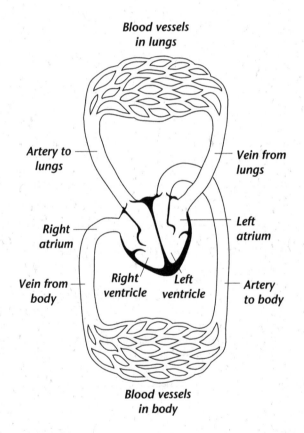

Blood vessels
in lungs

Artery to lungs

Vein from lungs

Right atrium

Left atrium

Vein from body

Right ventricle

Left ventricle

Artery to body

Blood vessels
in body

12. The largest artery in the body is called the _____.

Circulation and Respiration • *Reading/Notetaking Guide*

Arteries (pp. 544–545)

13. What is the structure of an artery?

_____

_____

_____

_____

14. Arteries carry blood away from the _____ .

15. Is the following sentence true or false? The coronary arteries provide the stomach with its blood supply. _____

16. Circle the letter of each sentence that is true about pulse.

a. The faster your heart beats, the slower your pulse will be.
b. Pulse is caused by the expanding and narrowing of artery walls.
c. When you count pulse beats, you are also counting heartbeats.
d. You can feel pulse in veins but not in arteries.

17. Is the following sentence true or false? Arteries control the amount of blood that different organs receive. _____

Capillaries (p. 545)

18. What important thing happens in the capillaries?

_____

_____

_____

19. One process in which materials are exchanged between the blood and the body cells is _____ .

Circulation and Respiration • *Reading/Notetaking Guide*

The Body's Transport System *(continued)*

Veins (p. 546)

20. What job do veins carry out?

_____

_____

_____

21. What three things help push blood through veins?

a. _____

b. _____

c. _____

22. Is the following sentence true or false? The walls of veins are generally much thinner than those of the arteries. _____

Blood Pressure (pp. 546–547)

23. What is blood pressure?

_____

_____

24. As blood moves away from the heart, does the blood pressure increase or decrease? _____

25. Circle the letter of the name of the instrument that measures blood pressure.

a. stethoscope
b. X-ray machine
c. sphygmomanometer
d. mercury

Blood and Lymph

Key Concepts

- What are the components of blood?

- What determines the type of blood that a person can receive in a transfusion?

- What are the structures and functions of the lymphatic system?

Blood is made up of four components: plasma, red blood cells, white blood cells, and platelets.

Plasma is the liquid part of blood. Plasma is mostly water, but 10 percent is made of dissolved materials. Plasma carries nutrients, such as glucose, fats, vitamins, and minerals. Many wastes are carried away from cells by plasma.

Red blood cells carry oxygen from the lungs to the body cells. A red blood cell is made mostly of **hemoglobin.** Hemoglobin is an iron-containing protein that binds chemically to oxygen molecules. Red blood cells are produced in the bone marrow and have no nuclei.

White blood cells are the body's disease fighters. They are bigger than red blood cells and have nuclei. Some white blood cells alert the body when disease-causing organisms invade. Others produce chemicals to fight the invaders. Some surround and kill the disease-causing organisms.

Platelets are cell fragments that help form blood clots. They collect and stick to any site where a blood vessel is cut. Platelets then release chemicals that cause the production of the chemical fibrin. Fibrin weaves a net of fibers across the wound. The net traps blood cells and a clot is formed.

There are four major types of blood. Each type has different marker molecules. Blood type A has the A marker, and blood type B has the B marker. Blood type AB has both the A and B markers. Blood type O has no markers. Your plasma contains clumping agents that make cells with foreign markers clump together. **The marker molecules on your red blood cells determine your blood type and the type of blood that you can safely receive in transfusions.** People with type A blood can receive transfusions of blood that does not have a B marker: type A or O blood. People with type B blood can receive transfusions of blood that does not have an A marker: type B or O. People with type AB blood have no clumping proteins. They can receive all blood types. People with type O blood have both anti-A and anti-B clumping proteins. They can only receive type O blood.

Red blood cells also contain another marker, called the Rh factor. A person's blood type can either be Rh negative or Rh positive.

In the capillaries, some fluid moves out of the cardiovascular system and into the surrounding tissues. The fluid moves into the body's drainage system, called the **lymphatic system. The lymphatic system is a network of veinlike vessels that returns the fluid to the bloodstream.** When the fluid enters the lymphatic system, it is called **lymph. Lymph nodes** are small knobs of tissue that filter the lymph as it passes through.

Circulation and Respiration ▪ *Reading/Notetaking Guide*

Blood and Lymph (pp. 549–555)

This section explains the components of blood and describes the jobs performed by the different parts of blood. This section also describes the lymphatic system.

Use Target Reading Skills

As you read the section about blood, write the main idea in the graphic organizer below. Then, write four supporting details that give examples of the main idea.

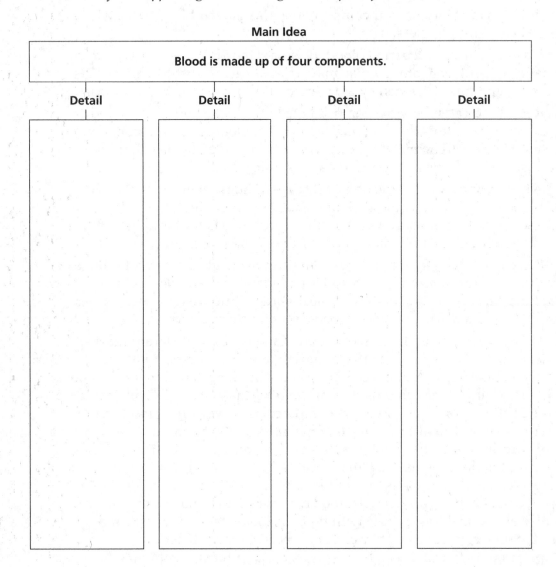

Main Idea

Blood is made up of four components.

Detail   Detail   Detail   Detail

Name _____ Date _____ Class _____

Blood (pp. 549–552)

1. What is the name for the liquid part of blood? _____

2. Complete the concept map below by naming the types of cells that are found in blood.

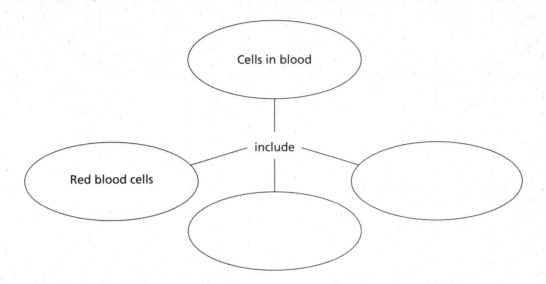

3. What is plasma mostly made up of? _____

4. List three kinds of materials that are carried in plasma.

    a. _____

    b. _____

    c. _____

5. What job do red blood cells perform in the body?
    _____
    _____
    _____

6. What is hemoglobin, and where is it found?
    _____
    _____
    _____
    _____

7. What is the job of white blood cells? _____
    _____

Circulation and Respiration ▪ *Reading/Notetaking Guide*

Blood and Lymph (continued)

8. List four ways in which white blood cells are different from red blood cells.

   a. _____

   b. _____

   c. _____

   d. _____

9. Is the following sentence true or false? Platelets are pieces of cells. _____

10. Describe how a blood clot forms. _____

    _____

    _____

Blood Types (pp. 553–554)

11. What is a blood transfusion? _____

    _____

12. Why can't a person with blood type A safely receive a transfusion of blood type B?

    _____

    _____

13. What is the Rh factor? _____

    _____

Match the blood type with the kinds of clumping proteins in its plasma.

	Blood Type	Clumping Proteins in Its Plasma
____	14. A	a. no clumping proteins
____	15. B	b. anti-B proteins
____	16. AB	c. both anti-A and anti-B proteins
____	17. O	d. anti-A proteins

The Lymphatic System (pp. 554–555)

18. What is the lymphatic system? _____

    _____

19. The fluid inside the lymphatic system is called _____.

20. How do lymph nodes help fight disease? _____

    _____

Chapter 14 Circulation and Respiration ▪ *Section 3 Summary*

The Respiratory System

Key Concepts

▪ What are the functions of the respiratory system?

▪ What structures does air pass through as it travels to the lungs?

▪ What happens during gas exchange and breathing?

The respiratory system moves oxygen from the outside environment into the body. It also removes carbon dioxide and water from the body.

Respiration is the process in which oxygen and glucose undergo a complex series of chemical reactions inside cells. Respiration, which is also called cellular respiration, releases the energy that fuels growth and other cell processes. Respiration is different from breathing, which is the movement of air into and out of the lungs. Respiration also produces carbon dioxide and water, which are eliminated by the respiratory system.

As air travels from the outside environment to the lungs, it passes through the following structures: nose, pharynx, trachea, and bronchi. Air enters the body through your nostrils and then moves into the nasal cavities. Some of the cells lining the nasal cavities produce mucus. Mucus cleans, warms, and moistens air you breathe. The inside of the nose is lined with cilia. **Cilia** (singular *cilium*) are tiny hairlike extensions that can move together. They sweep the mucus into the throat where it is swallowed.

Air moves from the nose downward into the throat, or **pharynx.** The **trachea,** or windpipe, leads from the pharynx to the lungs. The walls of the trachea are made of rings of cartilage that keep it open. The trachea is lined with cilia and mucus. The cilia in the trachea move the mucus toward the pharynx, where it is swallowed.

Air moves from the trachea into the **bronchi** (singular *bronchus*). The bronchi are passages that direct air into the lungs. The **lungs** are the main organs of the respiratory system. Inside the lungs, each bronchus divides into smaller and smaller tubes. At the end of the smallest tubes are bunches of alveoli (singular *alveolus*). **Alveoli** are tiny sacs of lung tissue specialized for the movement of gases between air and blood. Alveoli are surrounded by capillaries. **After air enters an alveolus, oxygen passes through the wall of the alveolus and then through the capillary wall into the blood. Carbon dioxide and water pass from the blood into the alveoli. This process is known as gas exchange.**

The **diaphragm** is a large, dome-shaped muscle at the base of the lungs. **When you breathe, the actions of your rib muscles expand or contract your chest, causing air to flow in or out.**

The **larynx,** or voice box, is located at the top of the trachea. Your **vocal cords** are two folds of connective tissue that stretch across the opening of the larynx. The vocal cords vibrate when air passes over them. This produces the sound of your voice.

Circulation and Respiration · *Reading/Notetaking Guide*

The Respiratory System (pp. 556–564)

This section describes the parts of the respiratory system and how they work to help you breathe and speak.

Use Target Reading Skills

As you read, complete the flowchart below to show the path of air in the respiratory system. Write each step of the process in a separate box in the order in which it occurs.

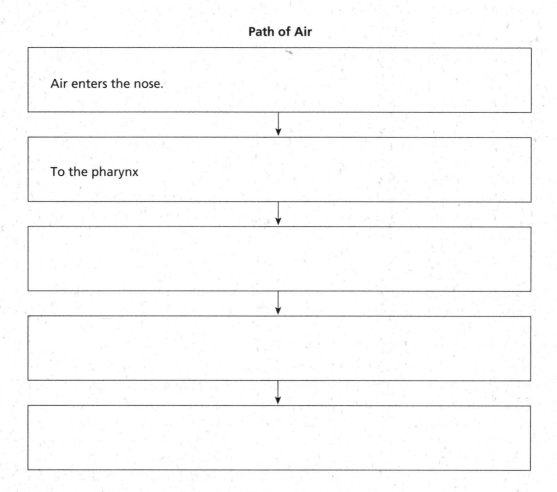

Path of Air

Air enters the nose.

↓

To the pharynx

↓

↓

↓

Respiratory System Functions (pp. 557–558)

1. Circle the letter of each sentence that is true about the air you breathe.

   a. The air you breathe is part of the Earth's atmosphere, the blanket of gases that surrounds Earth.

   b. Oxygen makes up about 78 percent of the gases in the atmosphere.

   c. Your body uses all of the air that you breathe into your lungs.

   d. Most of the air you breathe in goes back into the atmosphere when you exhale.

Circulation and Respiration ▪ *Reading/Notetaking Guide*

2. What are two functions of the respiratory system?

   a. _____

   b. _____

3. _____ is needed for the energy-releasing chemical reactions that take place inside your cells.

4. What is respiration?

   _____

   _____

   _____

5. List three products of respiration.

   a. _____   b. _____

   c. _____

6. Is the following sentence true or false? To a scientist, *breathing* and *respiration* mean the same thing. _____

7. Circle the letters of the organ systems that make respiration possible.

   a. circulatory system
   b. reproductive system
   c. respiratory system
   d. digestive system

The Path of Air (pp. 558–560)

8. Is the following sentence true or false? When you breathe in air, you also breathe in dust, pollen, and microorganisms. _____

The Respiratory System *(continued)*

9. Complete the flowchart to show the path of air as it travels to the lungs.

The Path of Air

> Air enters the body through two _____ ,
> or openings, in the nose.

↓

> Air moves through the _____ , which
> is also a part of the digestive system.

↓

> Air moves into the _____ , or windpipe.

↓

> Air moves through the _____ ,
> passages that direct air into the lungs.

10. What does a sneeze do?

_____

_____

11. Another name for the pharynx is the _____ .

Match the parts of the nose with their functions.

Parts	Functions
____ **12.** nostrils	**a.** Moistens the air and traps particles in the air
____ **13.** nasal cavities	**b.** Openings in the nose through which air enters
____ **14.** mucus	**c.** Tiny hairlike extensions that sweep mucus into the throat
____ **15.** cilia	**d.** Spaces lined with cilia and mucus

Circulation and Respiration • *Reading/Notetaking Guide*

16. Circle the letter of each body part that is connected to the pharynx.

    a. stomach

    b. nose

    c. mouth

    d. eyes

17. The walls of the trachea are made up of rings of _____ that strengthen the trachea and keep it open.

18. Is the following sentence true or false? The cilia and mucus in the trachea sweep upward, moving the mucus toward the nose, where it is sneezed out. _____

19. If food enters the trachea, a person can _____.

20. Circle the letter of the respiratory organs that the air reaches after the bronchi.

    a. trachea

    b. nose

    c. lungs

    d. pharynx

21. Is the following sentence true or false? Inside the lungs, each bronchus divides into smaller and smaller tubes. _____

22. What happens in the alveoli?

_____

_____

Gas Exchange (pp. 561–562)

23. What occurs during the process of gas exchange?

_____

_____

_____

24. Why can the lungs absorb a large amount of oxygen?

_____

_____

_____

Circulation and Respiration · *Reading/Notetaking Guide*

The Respiratory System *(continued)*

How You Breathe (pp. 562–564)

25. Is the following sentence true or false? The more oxygen you need, the more slowly you breathe. _____

26. What is the diaphragm? _____

_____

27. Complete the cycle diagram to show the process of breathing.

Rib muscles and diaphragm contract, making the chest cavity _____ .

The pressure of the air inside the lungs _____ .

Air rushes into the chest, and you _____ .

The rib muscles and diaphragm relax, and the chest cavity becomes _____ .

The air is squeezed out of the _____ , and you exhale.

28. Another name for the voice box is the _____ .

29. What are vocal cords?

_____

_____

_____

30. How do vocal cords create your voice?

_____

_____

_____

_____

Chapter 14 Circulation and Respiration • *Section 4 Summary*

Cardiovascular and Respiratory Diseases

Key Concepts

■ What are some diseases of the cardiovascular system?

■ What are some diseases of the respiratory system?

Cardiovascular disease is the leading cause of death in the United States. **Diseases of the cardiovascular system include atherosclerosis and hypertension.**

Atherosclerosis is a condition in which an artery wall thickens due to the buildup of fatty materials. One of these materials is a waxy, fatlike substance called cholesterol. Atherosclerosis restricts blood flow in the affected arteries.

If atherosclerosis develops in the coronary arteries that supply the heart, the heart muscle receives less blood. This condition may lead to a **heart attack**. Cells die in the part of the heart that does not receive blood. This permanently damages the heart.

Hypertension is a disorder in which a person's blood pressure is consistently higher than normal. Hypertension makes the heart work harder. It also may damage the walls of the blood vessels over time. People with hypertension often have no obvious symptoms to warn them. Hypertension is closely related to atherosclerosis. As the arteries narrow, blood pressure increases. Sometimes atherosclerosis and hypertension may lead to a stroke. A **stroke** is the death of brain tissue that can result when a blood vessel in the brain either is blocked by a clot or bursts.

Smoking damages the respiratory system and strains the circulatory system, resulting in disease. Some chemicals in tobacco smoke get into the blood and cause problems in the circulatory system, including atherosclerosis. Compared to nonsmokers, smokers are more than twice as likely to have heart attacks.

Respiratory diseases—also called pulmonary diseases—include emphysema, lung cancer, chronic bronchitis, asthma, and pneumonia. The chemicals in tobacco smoke damage lung tissue and breathing passages. **Emphysema** is a disease that destroys lung tissue and causes difficulty breathing. People with emphysema do not get enough oxygen and cannot adequately eliminate carbon dioxide.

Cigarette smoke contains more than 50 chemicals that cause cancer. Tumors take away space in the lungs that is used for gas exchange. Lung cancer is difficult to detect early enough for effective treatment.

Bronchitis is an irritation of the breathing passages. The small passages become narrower than normal and may be clogged with mucus. Long-term, or chronic, bronchitis can cause permanent damage to the breathing passages.

Asthma is a disorder in which the airways in the lungs narrow significantly. This narrowing causes wheezing and shortness of breath. **Pneumonia** is an infection in which fluids accumulate in the alveoli, decreasing the lungs' ability to take in oxygen and remove carbon dioxide.

Circulation and Respiration · *Reading/Notetaking Guide*

Cardiovascular and Respiratory Diseases (pp. 566–573)

This section describes diseases of the cardiovascular and respiratory systems.

Use Target Reading Skills

As you read, take notes on the main ideas and important details. Think about the Key Concepts and Key Terms. Use the graphic organizer to help you take notes.

Question	Answer
What are some cardiovascular diseases?	

Cardiovascular Diseases (pp. 567–569)

1. What is atherosclerosis? _____

_____

_____

2. What is cholesterol? _____

_____

Circulation and Respiration ▪ *Reading/Notetaking Guide*

3. Complete the flowchart below, which describes what can happen when atherosclerosis develops in the coronary arteries.

Atherosclerosis

Atherosclerosis develops in coronary arteries.

↓

Heart muscle receives less _____ , and therefore its cells receive less _____ .

↓

A(n) _____ occurs, which means that blood flow to part of the heart is cut off.

4. What is hypertension?

_____

_____

_____

5. Give two reasons why hypertension is a serious problem.

_____

_____

_____

_____

6. What is done to treat hypertension?

_____

_____

_____

Circulation and Respiration · *Reading/Notetaking Guide*

Cardiovascular and Respiratory Diseases (*continued*)

Health Problems and Smoking (pp. 570–573)

7. What are tar, carbon monoxide, and nicotine?_____

_____

8. Circle the letter of each sentence that is true about the effects of tobacco smoke.

    a. Tobacco smoke does not harm the respiratory system.

    b. Smokers cough frequently because their cilia cannot sweep away mucus.

    c. Smokers do not get as much oxygen because mucus buildup blocks air flow into the lungs.

    d. Heavy smokers can easily take part in vigorous sports.

9. List four respiratory problems that result from long-term smoking.

    a._____ **b.**_____

    c._____ **d.**_____

10. Is the following sentence true or false? Long-term, or chronic, bronchitis has no effect on the breathing passages. _____

11. A serious disease that destroys lung tissue and causes difficulty in breathing is _____.

12. What causes emphysema?

_____

_____

_____

13. Is the following sentence true or false? Cigarette smoke has over 50 different chemicals that cause cancer. _____

14. How do the chemicals in tobacco smoke affect blood vessels?

_____

_____

_____

_____

15. Is the following sentence true or false? Smokers are more likely to have heart attacks than nonsmokers. _____

How the Nervous System Works

Key Concepts

- What are the functions of the nervous system?

- What is the structure of a neuron and what kinds of neurons are found in the body?

- How do nerve impulses travel from one neuron to another?

The nervous system receives information about what is happening both inside and outside your body. It also directs the way in which your body responds to this information. In addition, the nervous system helps maintain homeostasis.

A **stimulus** is any change or signal in the environment that can make an organism react. After your nervous system analyzes a stimulus, it causes a response. A **response** is what your body does in reaction to a stimulus.

The cells that carry information through your nervous system are called **neurons,** or nerve cells. The message that a neuron carries is called a **nerve impulse.**

A neuron has a large cell body that contains the nucleus, threadlike extensions called dendrites, and an axon. The **dendrites** carry impulses toward the cell body. The **axon** carries impulses away from the cell body. Axons and dendrites are sometimes called nerve fibers. A bundle of nerve fibers is called a **nerve.**

Different kinds of neurons perform different functions. **Three kinds of neurons are found in the body—sensory neurons, interneurons, and motor neurons.** Together they make up the chain of nerve cells that carry an impulse through the nervous system.

A **sensory neuron** picks up stimuli from the internal or external environment and converts each stimulus into a nerve impulse. An **interneuron** is a neuron that carries nerve impulses from one neuron to another. A **motor neuron** sends an impulse to a muscle or gland, and the muscle or gland then reacts in response.

Nerve impulses begin in a dendrite, move toward the cell body, and then move down the axon. A nerve impulse travels along the neuron in the form of electrical and chemical signals.

The axon tip ends at a synapse. A **synapse** is the junction between each axon tip and the next structure. A small gap separates these two structures. **For a nerve impulse to be carried along at a synapse, it must cross the gap between the axon and the next structure. The axon tips release chemicals that carry the impulse across the gap.**

The Nervous System ▪ *Reading/Notetaking Guide*

How the Nervous System Works (pp. 544–546)

This section describes what the nervous system does in the body. It also tells how nerve impulses travel.

Use Target Reading Skills

As you read, identify the main idea of the section and three details that support the main idea. Use the graphic organizer below to list the main ideas and supporting details.

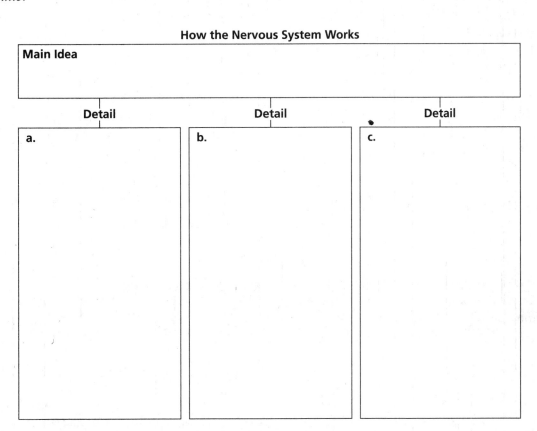

How the Nervous System Works

Main Idea

Detail	Detail	Detail
a.	b.	c.

Functions of the Nervous System (pp. 544–545)

1. List three jobs of the nervous system.

   a. _____

   b. _____

   c. _____

2. Is the following sentence true or false? You can move without your nervous system. _____

The Nervous System ▪ *Reading/Notetaking Guide*

How the Nervous System Works *(continued)*

3. From what two places does the nervous system receive information?

   a._____ b._____

4. Circle the letter of a change in the environment that can make an organism react.

   a. response
   b. stimulus
   c. homeostasis
   d. nerve impulse

5. Is the following true or false? All nervous system responses are voluntary, or under your control. _____

6. How does the nervous system help maintain homeostasis?

   _____

   _____

   _____

The Neuron (p. 546)

Match each term with its definition.

Terms	Definitions
_____ **7.** axon	**a.** The message that a nerve cell carries
_____ **8.** dendrite	**b.** An extension from a nerve cell that carries impulses toward the nerve cell
_____ **9.** neuron	**c.** An extension from a nerve cell that carries impulses away from the nerve cell
_____ **10.** nerve impulse	**d.** A cell that carries information through the nervous system

11. Is the following sentence true or false? A neuron can have only one axon.

    _____

12. A bundle of nerve fibers is called a(n) _____.

The Nervous System • *Reading/Notetaking Guide*

How a Nerve Impulse Travels (pp. 546–548)

13. Complete the flowchart to show the path of a nerve impulse.

Path of a Nerve Impulse

The telephone rings. Nerve impulses begin when a. _____ in the ear picks up the stimulus of the telephone ringing.

↓

The nerve impulse moves to b. _____ in the brain. The c. _____ interprets the impulses and decides to answer the phone.

↓

Nerve impulses from the brain move to d. _____. The muscles contract in response, and you pick up the telephone.

14. The junction where one neuron can transfer an impulse to another structure is called a(n) _____.

15. How does a nerve impulse cross the gap between the axon and the next structure?

_____

_____

Divisions of the Nervous System

Key Concepts

- What are the structures and functions of the central nervous system?

- What are the structures and functions of the peripheral nervous system?

- What is a reflex?

- What are two ways in which the nervous system can be injured?

Your nervous system has two divisions that work together. The **central nervous system** consists of the brain and spinal cord. The **peripheral nervous system** consists of all the nerves located outside of the central nervous system.

The central nervous system is the control center of the body and includes the brain and the spinal cord. The **brain,** located in the skull, is the part of the central nervous system that controls most functions in the body. The **spinal cord** is the thick column of nerve tissue that links the brain to most of the nerves in the peripheral nervous system.

There are three main regions of the brain that receive and process information. These are the cerebrum, the cerebellum, and the brain stem. The **cerebrum** interprets input from the senses, controls movement, and carries out complex mental processes such as learning and remembering. It is the largest part of the brain. The cerebrum is divided into a left half and a right half. The left half controls the right side of the body, and the right half controls the left side of the body.

The **cerebellum** coordinates the actions of your muscles and helps you keep your balance. The **brain stem** controls your body's involuntary activities such as breathing and heartbeat.

The peripheral nervous system consists of a network of nerves that branch out from the central nervous system and connect it to the rest of the body. The peripheral nervous system is involved in various actions, both voluntary and involuntary. A total of 43 pairs of nerves make up the peripheral nervous system.

The nerves of the peripheral nervous system can be divided into the somatic and autonomic nervous systems. The nerves of the **somatic nervous system** control voluntary actions—activities you can choose to do or not do. Nerves of the **autonomic nervous system** control involuntary actions such as adjusting the diameter of blood vessels.

A reflex is an automatic response that occurs very rapidly and without conscious control. Reflexes help to protect the body. In some reflex actions, skeletal muscles contract with the involvement of the spinal cord only—not the brain.

Concussions and spinal cord injuries are two ways in which the nervous system can be damaged. A **concussion** is a bruiselike injury of the brain. A concussion happens when soft tissue of the brain collides against the skull. Spinal cord injuries happen when the spinal cord is cut or crushed. Spinal cord injuries can result in paralysis, which is the loss of movement in some part of the body.

The Nervous System ▪ *Reading/Notetaking Guide*

Divisions of the Nervous System (pp. 550–557)

This section explains the two major parts of the nervous system. It also describes what a reflex is.

Use Target Reading Skills

Write a definition of each Key Term in your own words below.

central nervous system

_____

_____

peripheral nervous system

_____

_____

brain

_____

_____

spinal cord

_____

_____

cerebrum

_____

_____

cerebellum

_____

_____

brain stem

_____

_____

somatic nervous system

_____

_____

autonomic nervous system

_____

_____

reflex

_____

_____

concussion

_____

_____

Divisions of the Nervous System *(continued)*

Central Nervous System (p. 557)

1. Is the following sentence true or false? The central nervous system is the control center of the body. _____

2. The part of the central nervous system that controls most functions in the body is the _____.

3. The thick column of nerve tissue that links the brain to most of the nerves is the _____.

The Brain and Spinal Cord (pp. 552–554)

4. Is the following sentence true or false? All the neurons in the brain are interneurons. _____

5. What helps protect the brain from injury?

   a. _____

   b. _____

   c. _____

Match the parts of the brain with their functions. Each part of the brain may be used more than once.

	Functions	Parts of the Brain
____	**6.** Coordinates the actions of the muscles	**a.** cerebrum
____	**7.** Controls involuntary body actions, such as breathing	**b.** cerebellum
____	**8.** Interprets input from the senses	**c.** brain stem
____	**9.** Gives the body its sense of balance	
____	**10.** Carries out learning, remembering, and making judgments	

The Nervous System • *Reading/Notetaking Guide*

11. Is the following sentence true or false? The right half of the cerebrum controls the right side of the body. _____

12. Creativity and artistic ability are usually associated with the _____ side of the cerebrum.

13. The spinal cord is the link between the _____ and the _____.

14. What protects the spinal cord?

   a. _____

   b. _____

   c. _____

Peripheral Nervous System (pp. 554–555)

15. What does the peripheral nervous system consist of?

   _____

   _____

   _____

   _____

16. What is the function of the two groups of nerves making up the peripheral nervous system?

   Somatic nervous system: _____

   Autonomic nervous system: _____

The Nervous System · *Reading/Notetaking Guide*

Divisions of the Nervous System *(continued)*

Reflexes (pp. 555–556)

17. What is a reflex?

_____

_____

_____

18. Circle the letter of each sentence that is true about reflexes.

    a. In some reflex actions, the spinal cord, rather than the brain, directs the muscles to contract.

    b. Reflexes protect you from getting hurt badly.

    c. Nerve impulses move to the brain faster than they do to the spinal cord.

    d. The reflex action takes longer than it does for you to feel pain.

Nervous System Injuries (p. 557)

19. A bruiselike injury of the brain is called a(n) _____.

20. What can you do to decrease your chances of getting a brain injury?

_____

_____

_____

21. What happens when the spinal cord is cut or crushed?

_____

_____

_____

_____

Sight and Hearing

Key Concepts

- How do your eyes enable you to see?

- How do you hear and maintain your sense of balance?

Your eyes respond to the stimulus of light. They convert that stimulus into impulses that your brain interprets, enabling you to see. When rays of light first strike the eye, they pass through the **cornea,** the clear tissue that covers the front of the eye. Behind the cornea is the **pupil,** the opening through which light enters the eye. Around the pupil is the **iris,** a circular structure that regulates the amount of light entering the eye. Light that passes through the pupil strikes the lens. The **lens** is a flexible structure that focuses light. Light finally strikes the **retina,** the layer of receptor cells that lines the back of the eye. There are two types of receptor cells: rods and cones. **Rod cells** work best in dim light and allow you to see black, white, and shades of gray. **Cone cells** work best in bright light and allow you to see color. Light hitting the retina causes nerve impulses to begin. The optic nerve carries nerve impulses from the retina to the cerebrum. The brain interprets the signal and turns the image right-side up and produces one image.

The lenses in eyeglasses can help correct vision problems that result when the lens of the eye does not focus light properly. People with **nearsightedness** can see nearby objects clearly. They have trouble seeing distant objects. People with **farsightedness** can see distant objects clearly. They have trouble seeing nearby objects.

Your ears are the sense organs that respond to the stimulus of sound. The ears convert the sound to nerve impulses that your brain interprets. Sound is produced by material that is vibrating. The vibrations create waves. The ear is structured to receive sound waves.

The ear consists of three sections—the outer ear, middle ear, and inner ear. The outer ear helps gather sound waves. Sound waves move through the ear canal to the eardrum, which separates the outer ear from the middle ear. The **eardrum** is a membrane that vibrates when sound waves strike it. Three tiny bones in the middle ear—the **hammer, anvil,** and **stirrup**—transmit the vibrations from the eardrum to the cochlea in the inner ear. The **cochlea** is a snail-shaped tube lined with receptors that respond to sound. These receptors create nerve impulses that are carried through the auditory nerve to the brain. **Structures in your inner ear control your sense of balance.** Above the cochlea are the **semicircular canals,** which are the structures that are responsible for your sense of balance.

The Nervous System · *Reading/Notetaking Guide*

Sight and Hearing (pp. 558–564)

This section describes how your eyes enable you to see and how you hear.

Use Target Reading Skills

As you read, make an outline about the senses. Use the red headings for the main ideas and the blue headings for the supporting ideas.

The Senses
I. Vision
A. How light enters your eye
B.
C.
D.
E.
II.
A.
B.
C.
D.
E.

Vision (pp. 559–561)

Match the parts of the eye with their function.

Parts

_____ 1. iris

_____ 2. lens

_____ 3. cornea

_____ 4. pupil

_____ 5. retina

Functions

a. The layer of receptor cells that lines the back of the eye where nerve impulses begin

b. Regulates the amount of light entering the eye and gives the eye its color

c. The opening through which light enters the eye

d. The clear tissue that covers the front of the eye

e. Focuses light

Name _____ Date _____ Class _____

The Nervous System ▪ *Reading/Notetaking Guide*

6. Complete the flowchart to show how the eye sees objects.

How the Eye Sees Objects

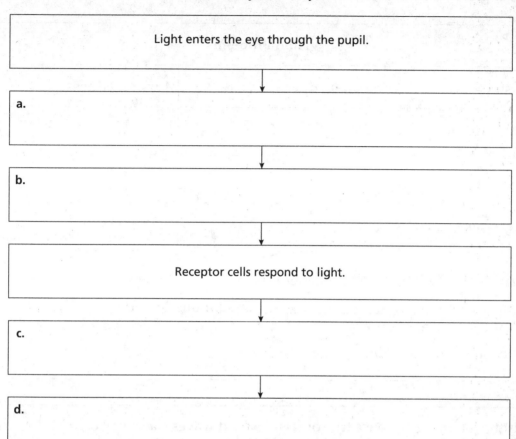

7. Is the following sentence true or false? Cone cells work best in dim light and enable you to see black, white, and shades of gray.

_____

8. What two things happen to the image in the cerebrum?

a. _____

b. _____ .

The Nervous System ▪ *Reading/Notetaking Guide*

Sight and Hearing *(continued)*

9. Complete the table to show the two kinds of vision problems.

Vision Problems		
Questions	**Nearsightedness**	**Farsightedness**
What is wrong?		
What causes it?		
How is it corrected?		

Hearing and Balance *(pp. 562–564)*

10. Ears convert _____, a stimulus, to nerve impulses that your brain interprets.

11. How are sounds made?

    _____

    _____

12. Is the following sentence true or false? Sound waves can travel only through air. _____

13. The outer ear is shaped like a(n) _____ to gather sound waves.

14. Circle the letter of the membrane that vibrates when sound waves strike it.

    a. outer ear
    b. hammer
    c. anvil
    d. eardrum

The Nervous System ▪ *Reading/Notetaking Guide*

Match the three main sections of the ear with their functions.

Main Section	Function

_____ **15.** outer ear

_____ **16.** middle ear

_____ **17.** inner ear

a. Vibrations pass from the hammer to the anvil to the stirrup.

b. Sound enters and reaches the eardrum.

c. Vibrations in the cochlea cause nerve cells to transmit signals to the brain.

18. What is the cochlea?

_____

_____

19. The structures in the ear that control your sense of balance are the

_____.

20. Is the following sentence true or false? The cerebellum analyzes the impulses to determine if you are losing your balance.

_____

Chapter 15 The Nervous System • *Section 4 Summary*

Smell, Taste, and Touch

Key Concepts

- How do your senses of smell and taste work together?
- How is your skin related to your sense of touch?

When you smell a cookie, receptors in your nose react to chemicals carried by the air from the cookie to your nose. When you take a bite of a cookie, your taste buds are stimulated. **Taste buds** are organs on your tongue that respond to chemicals in food.

The sense of smell and taste work closely together. Both depend on chemicals in food or in air. The chemicals trigger responses in receptors in the nose and mouth. Nerve impulses then travel to the brain, where they are interpreted as smells or tastes.

The nose can distinguish at least 50 basic odors. However, there are only five main taste sensations—sweet, sour, salty, bitter, and a meatlike taste called *umami*. When you eat, however, you experience a much wider variety of tastes because the flavor of food is influenced by both smell and taste.

The sense of touch is found in all areas of your skin. Your skin is the largest sense organ. **Your skin contains different kinds of touch receptors that respond to a number of stimuli.** The receptors that respond to a light touch are close to the surface of your skin. They tell you when something brushes against your skin, and they let you feel the texture of objects. Receptors deeper in the skin pick up the feeling of pressure. The skin also contains receptors that respond to temperature and pain. Pain is one of the body's most important feelings because it alerts the body to possible danger.

The Nervous System · *Reading/Notetaking Guide*

Smell, Taste, and Touch (pp. 565–567)

This section explains how your senses of smell and taste work together and how skin is related to your sense of touch.

Use Target Reading Skills

As you read, identify the main idea of the section and three details that support the main idea. Use the graphic organizer below to list the main ideas and supporting details.

Touch

Main Idea

Detail	Detail	Detail
a.	b.	c.

Smell and Taste (p. 566)

1. What are taste buds?

   _____

2. How do the senses of smell and taste work together?

   _____

   _____

   _____

3. Is the following sentence true or false? The nose can distinguish at least 100 basic odors. _____

The Nervous System ▪ *Reading/Notetaking Guide*

Smell, Taste, and Touch *(continued)*

4. List the five main taste sensations.

    a. _____ .

    b. _____

    c. _____ .

    d. _____

    e. _____

5. Why does food not seem as flavorful when you have a cold?

    _____

    _____

Touch (p. 567)

6. The sense of touch is found _____, making your
    _____ the largest sense organ.

7. Where are the receptors that respond to a light touch located, and what
    do they let you feel?

    _____

    _____

8. Is the following sentence true or false? Receptors deep in the skin sense
    the feeling of pressure.

    _____

9. Why is pain one of the body's most important feelings?

    _____

    _____

Chapter 15 The Nervous System • *Section 5 Summary*

Alcohol and Other Drugs

Key Concepts

- Which body system is immediately endangered by drug use?

- What are some commonly abused drugs and how does each affect the body?

- How does alcohol abuse harm the body?

To a scientist, a **drug** is any chemical taken into the body that causes changes in a person's body or behavior. **Drug abuse** is the deliberate misuse of drugs for purposes other than medical ones. Both legal and illegal drugs can be abused. **Most commonly abused drugs, such as marijuana, alcohol, and cocaine, are especially dangerous because they act on the brain and other parts of the nervous system.** In addition, long-term drug abuse can lead to addiction and other health and social problems. Most abused drugs can alter, or change, a person's mood and feelings. Mood-altering drugs affect patterns of thinking and the way in which the brain interprets information from the senses.

If a person takes a drug regularly, the body may develop a tolerance to the drug. **Tolerance** is a state in which a drug user needs larger and larger amounts of the drug to get the same effect. Tolerance can cause people to take an overdose and become unconscious or even die.

Repeated use of many commonly abused drugs can result in addiction. In **addiction,** the body becomes physically dependent on the drug. When the drug addict misses a few doses of the drug, the body reacts to the lack of the drug. The person is experiencing **withdrawal,** a period of adjustment that occurs when a person stops taking a drug. People can also become emotionally dependent on the feelings and moods produced by a drug.

Commonly abused drugs include depressants, stimulants, inhalants, hallucinogens, anabolic steroids, and alcohol. Many drugs affect the central nervous system, while others affect the overall chemical balance of the body. Depressants are drugs that slow down the activity of the central nervous system. **Stimulants** speed up body processes. Inhalants are inhaled, or breathed in. They can produce mood-altering effects. Hallucinogens can make people see or hear things that do not really exist. Some athletes try to improve their performance by taking **anabolic steroids,** synthetic chemicals that are similar to hormones produced in the body. They can cause mood changes and permanent physical damage.

Alcohol is a powerful depressant. It is quickly absorbed by the digestive system. The amount of alcohol in the blood is usually expressed as blood alcohol concentration, or BAC. Heavy drinking, especially over a long period, can result in significant health problems. **The abuse of alcohol can cause the destruction of cells in the brain and liver, and it can also lead to addiction and emotional dependence.** Abuse of alcohol can result in **alcoholism,** which is a disease in which a person is both physically addicted to and emotionally dependent on alcohol.

The Nervous System · *Reading/Notetaking Guide*

Alcohol and Other Drugs (pp. 568–573)

This section explains how drug abuse can affect the nervous system. It also describes how alcohol harms the body.

Use Target Reading Skills

As you read, identify commonly abused drugs and how they affect the body. Write the information in the graphic organizer below.

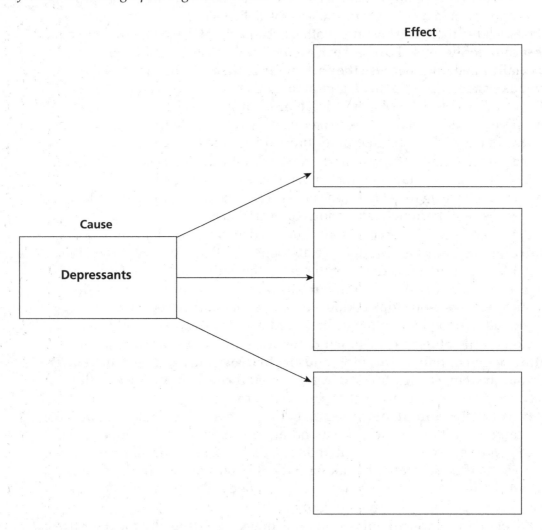

Introduction (p. 568)

1. Any chemical that causes changes in a person's body or behavior is a(n)

    _____.

The Nervous System • *Reading/Notetaking Guide*

Drug Abuse (pp. 568–569)

2. The deliberate misuse of drugs for purposes other than medical ones is called _____.

3. Circle the letter of each sentence that is true about drug abuse.

   a. Medicines can never be abused.
   b. Many abused drugs are illegal.
   c. The use of illegal drugs is not dangerous to the body.
   d. Abused drugs affect the body very shortly after they are taken.

4. The state in which a drug user needs larger and larger amounts of drugs to produce the same effect on the body is called

   _____.

5. Circle the letter of the period of adjustment that occurs when a person stops taking a drug.

   a. addiction
   b. tolerance
   c. withdrawal
   d. depressant

6. Is the following sentence true or false? When a person is emotionally dependent on a drug, the person is used to the feelings and moods produced by the drug. _____

7. How do mood-altering drugs affect the nervous system?

   _____

   _____

   _____

The Nervous System • *Reading/Notetaking Guide*

Alcohol and Other Drugs (continued)

Kinds of Abused Drugs (pp. 570–571)

Match the kind of drug with its characteristics.

Kinds of Drug	Characteristics
____ **8.** depressant	**a.** Produces mood-altering effects when breathed in
____ **9.** stimulant	**b.** Synthetic chemical similar to hormones used by athletes to improve performance
____ **10.** inhalant	
____ **11.** hallucinogen	**c.** Slows down the activity of the central nervous system
____ **12.** anabolic steroid	**d.** Can make people see or hear things that do not exist
	e. Speeds up body processes

13. What serious health problems can steroids cause?

_____

14. Why is steroid use especially dangerous for teenagers?

_____

Alcohol (pp. 572–573)

15. Circle the letter of the kind of drug that alcohol is.

    a. stimulant

    b. depressant

    c. anabolic steroid

    d. inhalant

16. Is the following sentence true or false? Alcohol is the most commonly abused drug in people aged 12 to 17. _____

17. Alcohol is quickly absorbed by the _____ system.

18. Is the following sentence true or false? About every two minutes, a person in the United States is injured in a car crash related to alcohol.

_____

19. What does a BAC value of 0.1 percent mean?

_____

20. Alcohol impacts a person's _____ processes, _____ , and _____ .

The Nervous System ▪ *Reading/Notetaking Guide*

21. How does the abuse of alcohol affect the body?

_____

_____

_____

_____

22. A disease in which a person is both physically addicted to and emotionally dependent on alcohol is called _____.

23. Is the following sentence true or false? Alcoholics must go through withdrawal to give up alcohol. _____

The Endocrine System

Key Concepts

- How does the endocrine system control body processes?

- What are the endocrine glands?

- How does negative feedback control hormone levels?

The endocrine system produces chemicals that control many of the body's daily activities. The endocrine system also regulates long-term changes, such as growth and development. The endocrine system is made up of glands. **Endocrine glands** produce and release their chemical products directly into the bloodstream. The blood then carries those chemicals throughout the entire body.

The chemical product of an endocrine gland is called a **hormone.** Hormones turn on, turn off, speed up, or slow down the activities of different organs and tissues. Because hormones are carried by blood, they can regulate activities in tissues and organs far from the glands that produced them. Hormones are released when nerve impulses travel to the brain and are interpreted. The brain then sends a nerve impulse to a specific endocrine gland. The gland then releases the hormone into the bloodstream.

A hormone interacts only with certain **target cells,** cells that recognize the hormone's chemical structure. A hormone and its target cell fit together the way a key fits into a lock. **The endocrine glands include the hypothalamus, pituitary, thyroid, parathyroid, adrenal, thymus, and pancreas. They also include the ovaries in females and testes in males.**

The nervous system and the endocrine system work together. The **hypothalamus,** a tiny part of the brain near the middle of your head, is the link between the two systems. Nerve messages controlling sleep, hunger, and other conditions come from the hypothalamus. The hypothalamus plays a major role in maintaining homeostasis.

The pituitary gland is located just below the hypothalamus. The **pituitary gland** communicates with the hypothalamus to control many body activities. Nerve impulses or hormone signals from the hypothalamus cause the pituitary gland to release hormones. Some hormones from the pituitary gland turn on other endocrine glands. Other pituitary hormones control body activities directly. Pituitary hormones regulate growth from infancy to adulthood and the amount of water in the blood.

The type of signal used in a heating system is called **negative feedback** because the system is turned off by the condition it produces. For example, suppose you set a thermostat at 20°C. If the temperature falls below 20°C, the thermostat signals the furnace to turn on. Once the furnace heats the room to the proper temperature, the thermostat sends a negative signal to the furnace that means "no more heat." Many hormones are controlled by a negative feedback system. **Through negative feedback, when the amount of a particular hormone in the blood reaches a certain level, the endocrine system sends signals that stop the release of that hormone.** Negative feedback is an important way that the body maintains homeostasis.

The Endocrine System and Reproduction • *Reading/Notetaking Guide*

The Endocrine System (pp. 576–581)

This section explains how the endocrine system works to control activities in the body.

Use Target Reading Skills

As you read, identify the effects of pituitary hormones. Write the information in the graphic organizer below.

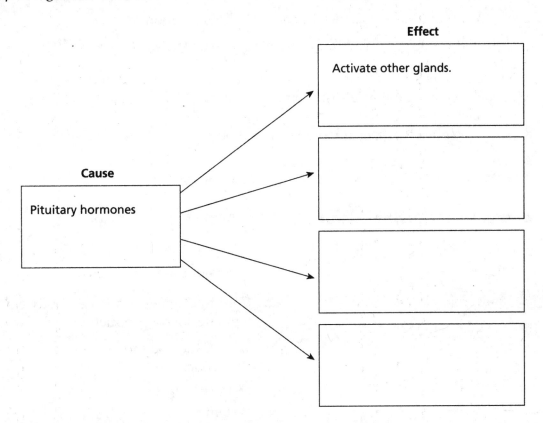

Effect

Activate other glands.

Cause

Pituitary hormones

Hormones and the Endocrine System (pp. 577–578)

1. What does the endocrine system control?

   _____

   _____

   _____

2. The endocrine system is made up of _____
   that produce chemicals that control body processes.

3. Is the following sentence true or false? Endocrine glands release their
   chemical products through delivery tubes. _____

The Endocrine System and Reproduction • *Reading/Notetaking Guide*

The Endocrine System (continued)

4. The chemical product of an endocrine gland is a(n)
_____, or chemical messenger.

5. How do hormones affect the body?

_____

_____

6. Circle the letter of each sentence that is true about hormones.
   a. Hormones can regulate only the tissues and organs near the glands that produce them.
   b. Nerve impulses from the brain can cause the release of hormones.
   c. In contrast to nerve impulses, hormones cause a slower, but longer-lasting, response.
   d. Any hormone can affect any organ in the body.

7. A hormone interacts only with certain _____, cells that recognize the hormone's chemical structure.

Functions of Endocrine Glands (pp. 578–580)

Match the endocrine glands with the functions of the hormones they produce.

Glands	Functions of the Hormones
____ 8. thyroid glands	a. Control changes in a male's body and regulate sperm production
____ 9. adrenal glands	b. Trigger the body to respond to emergencies
____ 10. ovaries	c. Helps the development of immune system
____ 11. testes	d. Control the release of energy from food molecules
____ 12. thymus	e. Control changes in a female's body that trigger egg development

13. Circle the letter of each sentence that is true about the hypothalamus.
   a. The hypothalamus links the nervous system and the excretory system.
   b. The hypothalamus is located on the kidneys.
   c. The hypothalamus sends nerve messages and produces hormones.
   d. The hypothalamus plays a major role in maintaining homeostasis.

The Endocrine System and Reproduction · *Reading/Notetaking Guide*

14. What is the pituitary gland?

_____

_____

_____

_____

15. Is the following sentence true or false? The pituitary gland releases hormones in response to nerve impulses or hormone signals from the hypothalamus. _____

Negative Feedback (pp. 580–581)

16. How does negative feedback work to control the amount of a hormone in the blood?

_____

_____

_____

_____

17. Complete the cycle diagram to show how thyroxine, a hormone produced by the thyroid gland, is regulated by negative feedback.

Hypothalamus senses cells need more energy.

Thyroid-stimulating hormone (TSH) is released by the
a. _____ gland.

Thyroid stops producing
e. _____ .

Thyroxine is produced by the
b. _____ gland.

Pituitary stops producing
d. _____ .

Hypothalamus senses
c. _____
have enough energy.

The Male and Female Reproductive Systems

Key Concepts

- What is sexual reproduction?

- What are the structures and functions of the male and female reproductive systems?

- What events occur during the menstrual cycle?

An **egg** is the female sex cell. A **sperm** is the male sex cell. The joining of a sperm and an egg is called **fertilization.** Fertilization is an important part of sexual reproduction, the process by which living things produce new individuals of the same type. **Sexual reproduction involves the production of eggs by the female and sperm by the male. The egg and sperm join together during fertilization.** When fertilization occurs, a fertilized egg, called a **zygote,** is produced. Chromosomes are structures in the cells that carry the information that controls inherited characteristics.

The male reproductive system is specialized to produce sperm and the hormone testosterone. The structures of the male reproductive system include the testes, scrotum, and penis. The **testes** are the organs in which sperm are produced. The testes also produce the hormone **testosterone,** which controls the development of male physical characteristics. The testes are located in an external pouch called the **scrotum.**

Sperm mix with fluids. This mix of sperm cells and fluids is called **semen.** Semen leaves the body through an organ called the **penis.** The male **urethra** runs through the penis. Semen and urine leave the body through the urethra.

The role of the female reproductive system is to produce eggs and, if an egg is fertilized, to nourish a developing baby until birth. The organs of the female reproductive system include the ovaries, fallopian tubes, uterus, and vagina. The **ovaries** are located slightly below the waist, one on each side of the body. The ovaries produce both egg cells and hormones. One hormone, **estrogen,** triggers the development of some adult female characteristics. Each ovary is located near a fallopian tube. The two **fallopian tubes** are passageways for eggs. Fertilization usually occurs in the fallopian tubes. Each month, one of the ovaries releases an egg. The egg moves through a fallopian tube, which leads to the uterus. The **uterus,** or womb, is a hollow muscular organ. If the egg has been fertilized, it remains in the uterus and begins to develop. The **vagina** is a muscular passageway leading to the outside of the body.

The **menstrual cycle** is a monthly cycle of changes that occurs in the female reproductive system. **During the menstrual cycle, an egg develops in an ovary. At the same time, the uterus prepares for the arrival of an embryo.** At the start of the menstrual cycle, an egg begins to mature in one of the ovaries, and the lining of the uterus begins to thicken. About halfway through the cycle, the mature egg is released from the ovary into a fallopian tube. This process is called **ovulation.** If it is not fertilized, the egg and the lining of the uterus break down. The extra blood and tissue of the thickened lining pass out of the body through the vagina. This process is called **menstruation.**

The Endocrine System and Reproduction • *Reading/Notetaking Guide*

The Male and Female Reproductive Systems (pp. 584–591)

This section describes the structures and functions of the organs in the male and female reproductive systems. It also explains the events in the menstrual cycle.

Use Target Reading Skills

As you read, make a cycle diagram that shows the menstrual cycle. Write each event of the process in a separate circle.

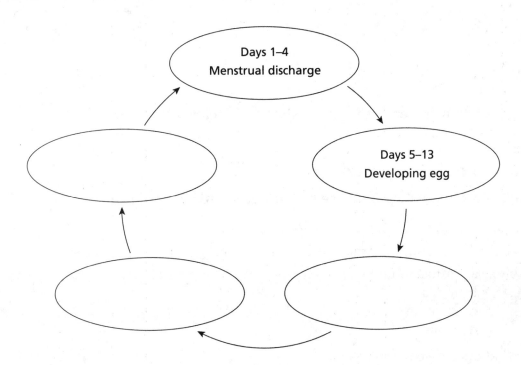

Days 1–4
Menstrual discharge

Days 5–13
Developing egg

Sexual Reproduction (p. 585)

Match each key term with its definition.

Terms	Definitions
____ 1. egg	**a.** The male sex cell
____ 2. sperm	**b.** A fertilized egg
____ 3. fertilization	**c.** The joining of a sperm and an egg
____ 4. reproduction	**d.** Carries the information that controls inherited characteristics
____ 5. zygote	**e.** The female sex cell
____ 6. chromosome	**f.** The process by which living things produce new individuals of the same type

The Endocrine System and Reproduction · *Reading/Notetaking Guide*

The Male and Female Reproductive Systems *(continued)*

7. Identify which is the egg and which is the sperm.

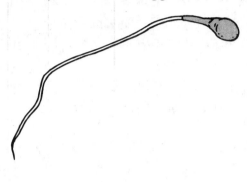 

a. _____   b. _____

8. Is the following sentence true or false? A sex cell has the same number of chromosomes as a body cell. _____

Male Reproductive System (pp. 586–587)

9. What is the male reproductive system specialized to produce?

a. _____   b. _____

10. Circle the letter of the organs in the male where sperm are produced.

    a. testosterone
    b. testes
    c. scrotum
    d. penis

11. What does testosterone control?

_____

_____

12. The testes are located in an external pouch of skin called the

_____.

13. Is the following sentence true or false? Sperm can develop normally only in slightly cooler temperatures than normal body temperature.

_____

14. What does semen provide to sperm?

a. _____

b. _____

15. Semen leaves the body through an organ called the

_____.

The Endocrine System and Reproduction ▪ *Reading/Notetaking Guide*

Female Reproductive System (p. 588)

16. What is the role of the female reproductive system?

_____

_____

_____

17. What do ovaries produce?

    a. _____

    b. _____

18. What does estrogen control?

_____

_____

_____

19. Complete the flowchart to show the path of an egg cell.

Path of an Egg Cell

_____ produces an egg cell.

⬇

The egg cell moves through the _____ where it can be fertilized.

⬇

The egg enters the _____ where it stays to develop if it's fertilized.

⬇

An unfertilized egg begins to break down and enters the muscular passageway leading to the outside of the body called the _____ , or birth canal.

The Endocrine System and Reproduction ▪ *Reading/Notetaking Guide*

The Male and Female Reproductive Systems (continued)

The Menstrual Cycle (pp. 589–591)

20. Circle the letter of how often an egg is released from the ovaries.

    a. daily

    b. weekly

    c. monthly

    d. yearly

21. The monthly cycle of changes that occurs in the female reproductive system is called the _____.

22. What occurs during the menstrual cycle?

_____

_____

_____

23. The menstrual cycle prepares the body for _____, the condition that begins after fertilization has taken place.

24. Circle the letter of each sentence that is true about menstruation.

    a. Menstruation lasts about 28 days.

    b. Hormones of the endocrine system control the menstrual cycle.

    c. All girls begin menstruation at the same age.

    d. Women stop releasing eggs from their ovaries at about the age of 50.

Pregnancy, Development, and Birth

Key Concepts

- What are the changes that occur to the zygote, embryo, and fetus during development?

- How is the developing embryo protected and nourished?

- What happens during childbirth?

- What changes occur as a person develops from infancy to adulthood?

A fertilized egg is called a zygote. After fertilization, the zygote begins to divide. **The zygote develops first into an embryo and then into a fetus. Cell differentiation leads to the development of specialized cells, tissues, and organs.** The developing human is called an **embryo** from the two-cell stage through the eighth week of development. Some cells of the embryo begin to fold into the center of the ball of cells at about three weeks. The layer into which a cell is located determines how it will differentiate. After the ninth week of development until birth, the embryo is called a **fetus.**

Soon after the embryo attaches to the uterus, membranes form. **The membranes and other structures that form during development protect and nourish the developing embryo, and later the fetus.** One membrane surrounds the embryo and develops into a fluid-filled sac called the **amniotic sac.** The fluid cushions and protects the developing baby. Another membrane forms, called the **placenta.** It links the developing embryo and the mother. The **umbilical cord** connects the embryo and the placenta.

After about nine months, the baby is born. **The birth of a baby takes place in three stages—labor, delivery, and afterbirth.** During the first stage of birth, called labor, strong muscular contractions of the uterus cause the cervix to enlarge, eventually allowing the baby to fit through the opening. During delivery, the second stage, the baby is pushed completely out of the uterus, through the vagina, and out of the mother's body. In the third stage, called afterbirth, contractions push the placenta and other membranes out of the uterus through the vagina.

The changes that take place between infancy and adulthood include physical changes, such as an increase in size and coordination, and mental changes, such as the ability to communicate and solve complex problems. Infancy is the first two years of life. During infancy, a baby's shape and size change greatly. Its nervous and muscular systems become better coordinated, and the baby develops new physical skills. Childhood is the life stage that begins at about two years of age. Children gradually become more active and independent, and they experience many physical and mental changes. Children gradually begin to change from a child to an adult during **adolescence.** Sometime between the ages of about 9 and 15 years, a child enters **puberty,** which is the period of sexual development in which the body becomes able to reproduce. After about the age of 30, a process known as aging begins.

The Endocrine System and Reproduction • *Reading/Notetaking Guide*

Pregnancy, Development, and Birth (pp. 592–599)

This section explains the changes that occur to the zygote, embryo, and fetus during development, what happens during birth, and what changes occur as a person develops from infancy to adulthood.

Use Target Reading Skills

After you read the section, reread the paragraphs that contain definitions of Key Terms. Use all the information you have learned to write a definition of each Key Term in your own words on a separate sheet of paper.

Development Before Birth (pp. 592–594)

1. After fertilization, the zygote develops first into an embryo and then into a(n) _____.

2. Is the following sentence true or false? The zygote begins to divide to make two and then four cells in the fallopian tube. _____

3. The growing mass of cells forms a hollow ball and attaches to the lining of the uterus, at which time the developing human is called a(n) _____.

4. The layer in which a cell of the embryo is located determines how it will _____.

5. Complete the table to show the development of the fetus.

The Development of the Fetus	
Time in Development	**What Is Happening**
Nine weeks	
From fourth to sixth month	
Final three months	

The Endocrine System and Reproduction • *Reading/Notetaking Guide*

Protection and Nourishment (pp. 594–595)

6. The fluid-filled sac that surrounds the embryo is called the

_____.

7. What is the placenta?

_____

_____

_____

8. What is the function of the umbilical cord?

_____

_____

_____

_____

9. Is the following sentence true or false? Substances, such as chemicals from tobacco smoke and alcohol, can pass from the mother to the embryo. _____

Birth (pp. 596–597)

10. List the three stages of the birth of a baby.

a. _____ b. _____

c. _____

11. Circle the letter of each sentence that is true about birth.

a. Strong muscular contractions, called labor, enlarge the cervix so that the baby fits through it.

b. During delivery, contractions push out the placenta and other membranes into the vagina.

c. After delivery, the umbilical cord is clamped and cut.

d. The baby is pushed completely out of the mother's body during afterbirth.

12. How does the baby's body adjust to the stress of the birth process?

_____

_____

_____

The Endocrine System and Reproduction ▪ *Reading/Notetaking Guide*

Pregnancy, Development, and Birth (continued)

Match the type of twins with its characteristics. Each type of twins may be used more than once.

Characteristics	**Type of Twins**
_____ **13.** Develop from a single fertilized egg	**a.** identical twins
	b. fraternal twins
_____ **14.** Develop when two eggs are released from the ovary and fertilized by two different sperm	
_____ **15.** Are no more alike than any brothers or sisters	
_____ **16.** Have identical inherited traits and are the same sex	

17. Is the following sentence true or false? Fraternal twins are never the same sex. _____

Growth and Development (pp. 598–599)

18. Is the following sentence true or false? During infancy, a baby's weight may double, and its nervous and muscular systems become better coordinated. _____

19. Circle the letter of the physical skill that babies develop first.

   a. crawl
   b. feed themselves
   c. walk
   d. hold up their heads

20. Circle the letter of each sentence that is true about childhood.

   a. Childhood begins at about the age of 13 years.
   b. Children become taller and heavier and become more coordinated.
   c. As they develop, children become less curious.
   d. Children show increased mental abilities and learn to read and solve problems.

The Endocrine System and Reproduction • *Reading/Notetaking Guide*

21. What is adolescence?

_____

_____

22. What is puberty?

_____

_____

23. Circle the letter of each physical change of puberty that occurs in girls.

    a. voice deepens

    b. ovulation starts

    c. sex organs develop

    d. hips widen

24. Circle the letter of each physical change of puberty that occurs in boys.

    a. hips widen

    b. sperm are produced

    c. hair grows on face

    d. voice deepens

25. After adolescence, _____ and _____ growth continue.

26. When does the aging process begin?

_____

27. How can the effects of aging be slowed?

_____

_____